# King's
# An Illustrated S
# 1933

CU00922479

## Introduction

I would like to thank the following people and organisations for their help:
Colin Bailey, Fraser Dawbarns, for his legal advice, John Allen for all his support, help
and advice on layout & proof reading, Lynn Museum (Norfolk Museums & Archaeology
Services), Norfolk County Council Library & Information Service (King's Lynn), Tony at
The Record Shop.

Other thanks go to everybody who has offered help, advice, assistance, support and who
have been kind enough to let me borrow their photos, without whom none of the books
could have been published. And special thanks to all at Clanpress for giving me so much
extra help and advice over the years.

The copyright of photographs from the Lynn News, West Norfolk Borough Council,
Norfolk Museum Services and the Eastern Daily Press is acknowledged and gratefully
appreciated.
Not all pictures were taken in 1933 but I have tried to use ones five years either side.
Also, owing to the shortage of good quality photos I have had to use photos from old
copies of the Lynn News.

* Some photos in the book have appeared in other publications.

Copyright © Bob Booth 2013

First Printed 2013 (80 years on from 1933)

Tricky Sam Publishing (Email: trickysampublishing@tiscali.co.uk,
Website: www.trickysampublishing.co.uk)

Printed by Clanpress, King's Lynn Tel: 01553 772737, Email: john@clanpress.co.uk

# Foreword (nothing changes)

The Great Depression or Great Slump, was a period of national economic downturn in the 1930s (in some ways similar to the current depression). It was Britain's largest economic depression of the 20th century. Britain's world trade fell by half (1929-33), the output of heavy industry fell by a third. At its depth in summer 1932, registered unemployed numbered 3.5 million, and many more had only part-time employment.

This accounted for about 25% being unemployed - compared with around 10% during the current crisis at its peak. In some areas (mainly the north) it reached 70% and many families depended entirely on payments from local government known as the dole.

Fortunately, since 1911, a compulsory national unemployment and health insurance scheme had been put in place in this country. This scheme had been funded through contributions from the government, the employers and the workers.

The scheme only paid out for 15 weeks. Anyone unemployed for longer than that had to rely on poor law relief paid by their local authority.

Millions of workers who had been too poorly paid to make contributions, or who had been unemployed long term, were left destitute by the scheme.

With the mass unemployment of the 1930s, contributions to the insurance scheme dried up, resulting in a funding crisis.

In August 1931 a new scheme was introduced with a fully government-funded unemployment benefit system. This unemployment benefit was subject to a strict means test and anyone applying for unemployment pay had to have an inspection by a government official to make sure that they had no hidden earnings or savings, undisclosed sources of income or other means of support.

From 1936 onwards, the National Government followed a policy of mass rearmament in the face of the rise of Nazi Germany. So by 1937 unemployment had fallen to 1.5 million - less than half that of 1932.

Some people became more affluent during the Depression because those still in work could buy more owing to falling prices. It is well known that a fall in demand causes prices to fall.

We knew that, since we were a manufacturing economy, we could afford to spend our way out of depression. Because, when the depression finally ended, we would become prosperous once again by selling to the world.

Unfortunately we cannot apply the same principles today because we manufacture very little compared with then. Plus other countries now own most of our large businesses (thanks to wholesale privatisation) and much profit made goes abroad.

Another difference between then and now is the currently rapidly increasing population size – this causes more demand for everything, particularly houses, petrol, schools, health services and household fuel to name a few.

*And higher demand means higher prices for everyone.*

A weekday late morning in High Street thought to be in the summer of 1937. Only one car (possibly a Morris 8) is driven down towards the Tuesday Market Place. Shops (from the right) are SG Street (music) - later to become East Anglian Savings Bank, Freeman, Hardy & Willis (footwear), George Goddard (outfitter), Winlove-Smith 'Café Imperial'(caterers) - later to become Woodcock's and Rivetts (drapers). The ladies hairdressing salons (left of photo at 86 High Street) are owned by Emmerson & Youngman.

## The 1930s

In the early 1930s the deposit to buy a house was dropped from 25% to 10%. A small terraced house cost around £500 and a good working wage was around £200 per year!

Lynn generated its own electricity (DC) at the Corporation Electricity Works, Kettlewell Lane. From 1934 a National Grid was set up to supply the whole country with a standard of 240 volts (AC).

New products to appear in shops included Bantam (the first instant coffee), Bournvita (1933), Lemon Barley Water (1935), Black Magic (1933), Kit Kat (1937), Mars Bars (1932), Aero (1935), Life-buoy soap (1933) and Dettol (1932) to name a few.

Breakfast cereals became very popular in the 1930s. Market leaders were Shredded Wheat (made at a new factory in Welwyn Garden City), Cornflakes, Rice Crispies and Puffed Wheat. Everyone had milk delivered.

In 1933 most comics were in black & white - Comic Cuts cost 1$^d$ but by the late 1930s most were in colour - Beano (1935), Dandy (1937), Hotspur (1939), plus dozens of others. The Target came out every Monday, cost a penny - and you could win half a crown (2/6).

In 1932 there was a boxed game (Olympic Games) which covered every event from the 100 yard sprint to the high jump. Monopoly came to Britain in 1936 from America - the New York streets were replaced with London streets.

Favourite Christmas annuals were Rupert, Mickey Mouse and Popeye. Woman's Own first appeared in 1932.

In 1934 the driving test became compulsory and would cost 7/6$^d$ (37½p). 'Cats eyes' first appeared on roads in 1935.

An Austin 7 car cost £120 but if you wanted a top-of-the-range British thoroughbred Lagonda it would cost £595. A cheap motor bike (the 147cc Wolf) cost £18 and a 2½HP Triumph cost £46.

A week's holiday in a boarding house in Great Yarmouth cost between 2 and 6 guineas - and there was no holiday pay while you were away. In 1933 a flight from London (Croydon) to Paris (Le Bouget) took over two hours and cost over £8. In 1936 Billy Butlin opened his first holiday camp. I believe his slogan was 'a week's holiday for a week's pay'.

The focal point in the home from 1930 was the wireless (radio). Popular makes included Philips, His Master's Voice (HMV), Murphy and Ekco.
The Radio Times cost $2^d$ and was bought by about 3 million set owners.
In 1933 a wireless licence cost 10/- and, if you had a dog, a licence for Fido cost $7/6^d$.

Films of the 1930s seem to show everyone smoking and it was advertised as a being healthy option! Favourite brands of the day included Player's Navy Cut, Senior Service, Craven A, Consulate and Du Maurier to name a very few. The working man's favourites were Will's Woodbines and Player's Weights. There was an incentive to buy with the inclusion of cigarette cards - a great favourite with children, who probably pestered their family to smoke to excess in order to get the set. These sets of footballers, trains, cars and many more usually comprised 50 cards.

Few people had a telephone so the only way to make contact with distant friends and relatives was by letter ($1½^d$) or postcard ($1^d$).
The forerunner to the email/text was the telegram (6 words for $6^d$).

In 1933 Malcolm Campbell reached a record land speed of 272 mph in Bluebird.
Henry Beck designed the new (now standard) underground map.
Class A4 steam locomotive 'Mallard' broke the record by reaching a speed of 126.4mph between Grantham and Peterborough in 1938.

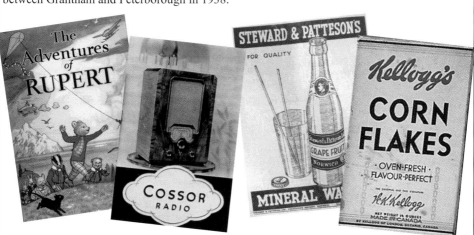

# Events of the 1930s

1930: The Convent opens in Goodwins Road.
Terrific gale strikes Lynn.
Highgate school re-opens after addition of two classrooms and heating system.

1931: Fire at Savages.
Severe earth tremors felt in Lynn.
British Legion Club opens.

1932: New St James Boys school opens on Hospital Walk.
A new club for the Lynn workless opens on Railway Road in the former United Methodists.
New Co-op bakery opens in Austin Street next to the Co-op dairy.
Jermyn's 60th anniversary.

1933: You can buy a new suit for £2-10s at Fifty Shilling Tailors in the High Street.
A traffic census on the Lynn – Hunstanton road reveals 7,058 vehicles a day.
New Post Office for Lynn under consideration.
Lightning causes a fire at Chapman & Co saw-mills on the Bentinck Dock.
Lynn Town Council passes Slum Clearance Scheme.
Sir Oswald Mosley addresses a meeting of the invidious British Union of Fascists.

### *The 1934 the summer train timetable to Hunstanton:*

|                  | AM   | AM   | AM    | AM    | AM    | PM    | PM   | PM   | PM   | PM   | PM   | PM   | PM   | PM    |
|------------------|------|------|-------|-------|-------|-------|------|------|------|------|------|------|------|-------|
| King's Lynn (dep) | 7.28 | 8.48 | 9.40  | 10.21 | 11.19 | 12.44 | 1.35 | 2.00 | 3.20 | 4.48 | 6.44 | 7.18 | 8.44 | 11.00 |
| North Wootton    | 7.33 | 8.53 | 9.47  | 10.28 | 11.26 | 12.51 | 1.42 | ...... | 3.27 | 4.55 | 6.51 | 7.25 | 8.51 | 11.07 |
| Wolferton        | 7.39 | 8.59 | 9.53  | 10.34 | 11.33 | 12.57 | 1.49 | 3.02 | 3.33 | 5.01 | 6.57 | 7.32 | 8.57 | 11.13 |
| Dersingham       | 7.44 | 9.06 | 9.58  | 10.39 | 11.37 | 1.02  | 1.54 | ...... | 3.38 | 5.08 | 7.02 | 7.37 | 9.02 | 11.18 |
| Snettisham       | 7.49 | 9.11 | 10.03 | 10.44 | 11.42 | 1.07  | 1.59 | ...... | 3.44 | 5.13 | 7.07 | 7.42 | 9.07 | 11.23 |
| Heacham          | 7.55 | 9.17 | 10.09 | 10.50 | 11.48 | 1.13  | 2.05 | 3.14 | 3.50 | 5.19 | 7.13 | 7.48 | 9.13 | 11.29 |
| Hunstanton (arr) | 8.04 | 9.22 | 10.14 | 10.55 | 11.54 | 1.21  | 2.10 | 3.20 | 3.56 | 5.25 | 7.20 | 7.53 | 9.19 | 11.34 |
|                  |      |      |       |       |       | S     | W    | W&S  | R    |      |      |      | R    | S     |

S=Saturdays only, W=Wednesday only, W&S=Wednesday & Saturday only and R =restaurant car (ex Liverpool Street).

1934: Two-on-a-cycle is banned!
Man found guilty of diddling a Diddlem Club[1].
Houses on the new Methuen Avenue Estate cost from £475.
Official opening of Labour Club in Chapel Street
Brooker's cycle and radio premises in Tower Street gutted by fire.
Lynn Corporation buy Gaywood Hall and 260 acres for £16,000. New school to be built.
RH Guest opens a new garage on Wootton Road.

1935: On February 9th The Queen opens the new ophthalmic block at Lynn.
On February 12th The King & Queen visit Lynn hospital to see the new wing and nurse's hostel.
Demolition of house on King Staith Square to make way for a new warehouse.
Three plans discussed to relieve traffic congestion at Tennyson Avenue railway crossing (subway, bridge or bypass).
Demolition of old property on the south side of Purfleet Street.
Lynn & District Gilbert & Sullivan Society presents 'Iolanthe'.
Belisha Beacons' first installed in the streets of the town.
New Burtons opens at 98-99 High Street.

1936: Death of King George V at Sandringham.
Plans to enlarge and improve the isolation hospital.
Theatre Royal destroyed by fire.
71 condemned houses under the slum clearance scheme are reprieved.
Total of 168 new houses have been completed on the Burlingham Estate[2] for families displaced under the slum clearance programme.
The new Clarkes Garage opens on Lynn Road.
The M&GN railway's office in Austin Street was closed as LNER takes over.
A new Territorial Hall is officially opened in Wellesley Street.
Including Gaywood the town's population was 20,583 (9,990 male and 10,593 female).

1937: St James Cinema burns down.
A man is fined 5/- for cycling without lights.
A man is fined 2/6d for carrying a friend on his bike.
Fines of 2/6 and 5/- issued to parents for school non-attendances.
New Ford 8 on sale at JF Davy for £105 (to compete with the Morris 8).
New quay opened by the Boal Wharfingers Ltd.
WH Johnson extends garage.

1938: West Norfolk & King's Lynn Hospital announce a contributory scheme for every form of treatment. Cost is 2d per week (or 10/- per year)

1939: Building of air raid shelters begins.
The new Victor Beesley (originally Charles Winlove-Smith) Café Imperial opens in High Street. After the war this became AB Woodcock (bakers).
The new General Post Office opens on Baxter's Plain.
Gaywood Park secondary school opens.

[1] *A diddlem club was a savings club formed by local residents e.g. a Christmas club.*
[2] *This was the name given to the area between Salter's Road and Bawsey Drain/Clark's Dyke, North Lynn.*

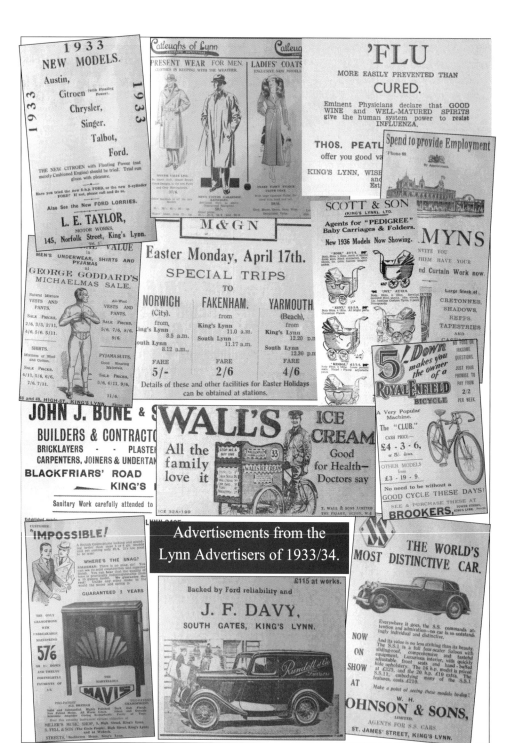

Advertisements from the Lynn Advertisers of 1933/34.

## KING'S LYNN
### SPEND-FOR-EMPLOYMENT COMMITTEE

# £10,000 CAMPAIGN.

Patron: His Worship the Mayor.

## GET THAT JOB DONE NOW AND INCREASE EMPLOYMENT.

Something must be done and done quickly to revive and stimulate our trade and industry, that local unemployed men may obtain work.

### DO YOUR BIT NOW

by placing orders for work at once instead of later in the year.

# IDLE MONEY CREATES UNEMPLOYMENT.

You can cause more men and women to be employed by repairing your property, painting and renovating your home and furnishings, overhauling your garden, etc.

Bring forward work of every kind and so

## FIND JOBS AT ONCE.

---

## SPEND FOR EMPLOYMENT COMMITTEE.

Patron: His Worship the Mayor.

# NOW IS THE TIME

To Plan and Order that Improvement in your HOUSE, GARDEN, BUSINESS.

Give an Unemployed Man the Chance to Work NOW.

Please signify your intention to help by signing and sending this advertisement

G. S. HAYHOW, Hon. Secretary,

Purdy's Court, High-st., King's Lynn

An Order for Work to increase Employment being placed by the undersigned.

Name ..........................

Address ..........................

---

## SINCE JANUARY.

The steady decline in the number of unemployed this year is shown in the following table:

| | |
|---|---|
| January | 2,903,065. |
| February | 2,856,638. |
| March | 2,776,184. |
| April | 2,697,634. |
| May | 2,582,879. |
| June | 2,438,108. |
| July | 2,442,175. |
| August | 2,411,137. |
| September | 2,336,727. |

Since January there has been a decrease in registered unemployment of over 566,000.

---

## LYNN'S UNEMPLOYMENT FIGURES.

### A SLIGHT IMPROVEMENT.

Lynn's unemployment problem is decreasing in intensity as the summer approaches, but it is still acute. Figures published on Tuesday morning, for the month ended April 24, show that Lynn Employment Exchange is not experiencing such a rapid fall as was hoped.

The building and allied trades remain busy but the high figure for casual workers shows little sign of depletion, while the trade of the port remains at the low level which it has experienced since Christmas. There are hopes of improvement in the near future, when various seasonal occupations relieve the pressure.

There are 1,290 persons on the register as against 1,325 last year. Details, compared with last year's figures:

| Men | | |
|---|---|---|
| wholly unemployed | 583 | against 602 |
| casual workers | 314 | ,, 325 |
| *non-claimants | 122 | ,, 122 |
| temporarily stopped | 56 | ,, 41 |
| totals | 1,075 | ,, 1,090 |

| Women | | |
|---|---|---|
| wholly unemployed | 61 | against 67 |
| casual workers | 3 | ,, 3 |
| *non-claimants | 72 | ,, 86 |
| temporarily stopped | 1 | ,, 6 |
| totals | 137 | ,, 162 |

| | | |
|---|---|---|
| Boys | 24 | ,, 26 |
| Girls | 54 | ,, 47 |

* Denotes those who have been registered as requiring employment but who are not receiving unemployment benefit.

---

1933 Advertisements appeared in the Lynn Advertiser to try and stimulate the local economy like the two on the far left.

*Above right:* Shows the national unemployment figures was about 25% of the total workforce in the country. Today (2013) it is less than 8%.

*Left:* The number of unemployed in Lynn was about 15% of the work-force - certainly better than the national average.

9

**This press announcement in August 1933 was that there would be a five year programme to eradicate the worst slums in the town.**

THE LYNN NEWS AND COUNTY PRESS

# HOW LYNN'S COURTS AND ALLEYS WILL BE SWEPT AWAY

## ALL ABOUT COUNCIL'S £200,000 SCHEME

### What Lynn Will Look Like In Five Years

### NEW HOUSES FOR NINE PER CENT. OF POPULATION

#### Slum Clearance Committee's Comprehensive Plans

THE HOUSES in Lynn's courts and alleys are to be demolished within five years. The Town Council signed their death warrant on Wednesday by passing the £200,000 scheme prepared by the slum clearance committee for submission to the Ministry of Health.

There are 512 of these houses, occupied by 1,890 men, women and children—nine per cent. of the population of the borough. These tenants will be re-housed in new dwellings on well-planned estates in the North and South ends of the town. These houses will be light, airy and convenient, with gardens front and back, and rents which a working man can pay. Compared with the dwellings to be demolished—well, there's no comparison!

The scheme was explained, discussed, questioned, commended, opposed, welcomed and regretted at the Council meeting on Wednesday, but when the vote was taken the result was 11-8 in favour of submitting it to the Ministry.

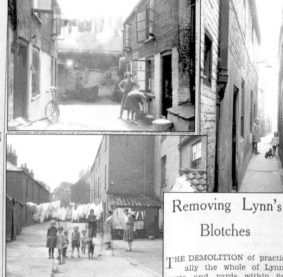

## Removing Lynn's Blotches

THE DEMOLITION of practically the whole of Lynn's courts and yards within five years is a prospect which we welcome wholeheartedly. The re-housing of about nine per cent. of the borough's population in new estates at the North and South ends of the town is a scheme which has our hearty support. The slum clearance committee has earned the gratitude of the community for tackling this long-standing problem so courageously. The Medical Officer and the Sanitary Inspector are to be congratulated upon preparing the necessary information so carefully and completely.

The prospect of getting 1,301 adults and 589 children out of these courts and alleys into light and airy modern dwellings with gardens will gladden the hearts of all who have the physical and moral health of the community at heart. Slums are the breeding place for diseases of the mind as well as of the body, and one of the saddest features of life in these wretched districts is that children are growing up amid conditions which are souring their fresh innocence, sapping their moral strength and warping their mental outlook. As the

# 1933 - the start of the clearance of the slums of Lynn

As the first part of the five year plan the first portion of its slum clearance was taken by Lynn Town Council in November 1933.

The areas considered for clearance were:

♦ Armes Yard (9 High Street - nine houses and associated outbuildings).
♦ Begley's Yard( 2 Providence Street - four houses and outbuildings).
♦ The area comprising Evett's Yard (37 Checker Street - four houses and out-buildings), Fleece Yard (55 Friars Street - eight houses and outbuild-ings), Broughton's Cottages (43 Checker Street - two houses and out-buildings).
♦ Southgate Court (Southgate Street - eleven houses and outbuildings).
♦ Payne's Court (8 Church Street - nine houses and outbuildings).
♦ Tower Court (39 St James Street - five houses).
♦ Church Street, one house.
♦ White House Cottages (26 London Road - five houses).
♦ Simpson's Yard and Crown's Yard (All Saints Street - four houses).
♦ The area comprising Crooked Lane, Union Place, Law's Yard, Miller's Court, Bridge Street, Saddleton's Yard and Crome's Yard - thirty five houses and outbuildings.

The Medical Officer of Health submitted a report that the houses in each of the areas are:

I. By reason of disrepair or sanitary defects unfit for human habitation.
II. By reason of their bad arrangement or the narrowness or bad arrangement of the streets, dangerous or injurious to the health of the inhabitants of the area.
III. The most satisfactory method of dealing with the conditions in the area is the demolition of all buildings in the area.

To house all the displaced families would require the building of 94 new homes (68 to be built off Wisbech Road and the other 26 elsewhere). The number of persons displaced would be about 358.

TOP: Theatre Royal not long before it burnt down in 1936. It was rebuilt and opened in 1939.
ABOVE: View of piling in preparation for the construction of a new grain silo for Vynne & Everett (maltsters) on King Staith Square in 1936.

TOP: Stonegate Street. One of the posters advertises 'Gibson's for Posters'. Mrs Ellen Gibson who had operated from High Street and now lived at in Stonegate Street was living in the adjacent house in1933.

ABOVE: Surrey Street looking from the corner of the Tuesday Market Place down towards Chapel Street.

If there are missing numbers in streets it can mean that the information was refused or the house was empty at the time the census was made or the property was let as several flats. Residents in many yards were not listed in 1933 but were shown in the 1936 census. The yards concerned are shown thus: **BRICK YARD\***

In 1933 Gaywood was still considered a village so is not shown in the census of Lynn. The Gaywood - Lynn boundary was where Lynn Road met Gaywood Road i.e. where the Hunstanton railway line crossed the road.

Up to the 1930s Gaywood stretched little more than ½ mile from the Hunstanton railway line and, like Lynn, had its share of yards of desperate housing.

Gaywood really expanded apace in the 1930s and by 1935 became part of Lynn.

The population of Lynn was 20,583 but this rose to 23,550 when Gaywood was included in 1935. The earliest census of properties and residents for the parish of Gaywood that have also been included is 1936.

Properties which fall into this category are shown thus: **METHUEN AVENUE♦**

## ABERDEEN STREET
*From 3 Extons Road*
2  Auker Robert John

## ALBERT AVENUE
*From 13 Albert Street*
### South side
1  Whitehouse Alfred
2  Scoon Scott
3  —
### West side
4  Abbott Tom
5  Tinkler Cyril Richard
6  Hoare Thomas M
7  Rayner Ernest
8  Shaw John William
9  Rhodes Edwin James
10  Gribble Walter  junior
11  Hoare Miss ME
12  Nokes Leonard
13  Barnard Herbert
14  Davison John Henry
15  Gribble Walter   senior
### East side
16  Eggett Frank
17  Clarke William
18  Moore Edward James
19  Eade George A

20  Nisbet James Cooper
21  Allen Arthur
22  Caston James Charles

## ALBERT STREET
*From 114 Norfolk Street to 34 Austin Street*
### West side
1  —
2  Simpson George Henry
2  Simpson W&A  (painters)
3  Hayes William T  (cork manufacturer)
4  Howard Mrs
5  Leggett Thomas Reginald
6  Fisher Miss GE
7  Granger Arthur Robert
8  Parker William
9  Bird Hubert Philip   senior
10  Bradnam Orlando R
11  Dye George Alfred
12  Dann William S
13  Hayes GW  FALPA (auctioneer)
*here are Albert Avenue & Albert Terrace*
14  Rains Mrs
15  Rix Frederick
15  Rix & Groom Ltd (coal dealers - office)
16  Fox Leopold
17  Pamment Mrs

14

Alexandra dock late 1930s.

## ALBERT STREET (continued)
### East side
18 Spinks Henry (grocer)
19 Rix James Henry
20 Wilson Reginald
21 **Albert PH** **(George Alfred Ward)**
   *here is East Street*
22 —
23 Smith Henry James (rent collector)
24 Franklin Maurice
25 Lane Frederick
26 Palmer Robert

### Johnson's Square
1 Stannard Mrs
2 Gittens Mrs
3 Hilton Miss
4 Wayte James C
5 Meggitt Edward
6 Crome William
7 Fayers James Edward
8 Hitchcock James Henry
9 Harper Mrs

10 Bullen Mrs
11 Doy Herbert Edgar
12 Gore Robert E
Simpson Alfred Charles (corn dealer)

## ALBERT TERRACE
*From 14 Albert Street to Albert Avenue*
### North side
1 Smith William
2 Fuller George
3 Bradford Ernest Harry
4 English Stanley
5 Dockerill Mrs
6 Tinkler Miss

## ALBION STREET
*From 20 Market Street to 15 Railway Road*
### West side
St. John's Schools (boys, girls & infants)
Parke Thomas G (motor engineer)
11 Adams Mrs
10 Culey William

## ALBION STREET (continued)

9 Gamble Frederick
8 Chilvers Mrs
*here is the Cattle Market*
15 Laight Mrs
14 Brown Herbert

### East side

Warner H & Son (heating engineers)
1 —
2 Hulford John
3 Taylor Frederick
4 Parker Turner W
5 Whiley Anthony
Johnson Benjamin James (decorator )
6 Crome Francis
7 Ward Miss
7a Furbank Mrs
6a Jackson John Richard

## ALEXANDRA DOCK

*From St. Ann's Fort*

King's Lynn Docks & Railway Co.
(Ivan J Thatcher, general manager)
Tassell Arthur L & Sons Ltd. (coal factors)
Feedstuffs Ltd. (corn merchants)
East Anglian Grain Co Ltd (corn
merchants)
Pattrick & Thompsons Ltd. (timber
merchants)
Stanton J T & Co. Ltd. (timber merchants)
Tinkler CR (vice-consul for Finland)
Eastern Roadways Ltd. (haulage
contractors)
Bowker James & Co. Ltd. (shipping agents)
East Anglian Grain Co. Ltd. (corn
merchants)
London, Midland & Scottish Railway
- WJ Bray (goods agent)
London & North-Eastern Railway (G E section)
- Jack Beeston (station master)
Krieken H Van & Co Ltd (steamship owners)

## ALL SAINTS STREET

*From 6 South Lynn Plain to
la Bridge Street*

### North-east side

1 Arrowsmith Albert W (butcher)
2 Johnson Robert Charles
3 Human Harlock
4 Dorman Bertie A
5 Knowles Gordon
6 Wilmore Alex
7 Snasdell Robert E (newsagent)
*here is Union Street*
8 Barnes Mrs W S (board residence)
9 Bruce Sidney
10 Tranter Mrs
11 Davies Emlyn
12 Moore Wilfred
13 Steward John
*here is Saddleton's Yard*
Shepherds Hall Mission Room
14 Thrower Edward
14a Brown Thomas A
*here is Simpson's Yard*
15 Mallett Mrs E
16 Clarke Fred
17 Regester Frank P
18 English Mrs SE

### South-west side

*here is The Friars*
Springall Hubert French (The Friars)
20 Toll Arthur
21 Norfolk Dairies (Alcock & Appleby)
22 Gibson Alfred
23 Begley Herbert E
24 Wagg George (boot repairer)
25 Hill Henry
26 Tilson James Everitt
27 Barrett Charles
28 Flint George Daniel
29 Barker George
30 Fordham Frederick (dairyman)
31 Behn Mrs JM

All Saint's Street 1933.

## ALL SAINTS STREET (continued)
32 Bennett Misses J&L
33 Whitehand Mrs Sarah (grocer)
34 Sadler Mrs N
35 Wickham Samuel
36 Rackham Misses C & E (shopkeepers)
37 Lubbock Miss L (stationer & post office)
38 Haycock Herbert E (hairdresser)
39 Powley Miss
40 Walker William

### ALLEN'S YARD
*From 47 Pilot Street*
2 Rake Charles

### ANDREW'S YARD
*From 4 Stonegate Street*

## ARCHDALE STREET
*From Eastgate Street*
### North side
1 Hendry George
2 Loasby William Thomas
3 Clitheroe Arthur
4 Scase Frederick
5 Miles Isaac
6 Hill William
7 Hythe Francis James
9 Wilson Mrs
10 Barnes George
11 Willimott Mrs
12 Gibbs George
13 Lemmon Arthur
14 Smith William
15 Spooner Tom
16 Beckham William
17 Clarke William Charles
18 Youngs George
18 Youngs Eric E (tailor)

## ARCHDALE STREET (continued)

19  Dawson William
20  Rolph Edward James
21  Giles Arthur
22  Robinson Alfred  (builder)

### South side

23  Raines John William
24  Brockbank James
25  Collins Robert
26  Slight Alfred S
27  Petts Matthew
28  Reeve Albert
29  Hubbard Harold E
30  Greenacre Tom
31  Manning Louis
32  Pedder Sidney Albert
33  Howell Mrs
34  Seaman George
35  Smith Jack
36  Hooke Albert
37  Steinforth Joseph
38  Kenny Thomas
39  Ketteringham John W
40  Richardson George

## ARGYLE STREET

*From 4 Somerville Road*

1  Riches James Edmonds
2  Faulkner Cecil Albert
3  Hooke Horace Vernon
4  Finbow Hubert W
5  Webb Thomas
6  Bowers Horace William
7  Peak William
8  Lee Sydney James
9  Poole Francis Henry
10  Stokes John Charles
11  Goodson William Gray
12  Gore Ernest Bertie
13  Hall Walter
14  Crome Hector Christopher
15  Franklin William

16  Fisher Charles
17  Thomas Algernon Percy

## ARME'S YARD

*From 9 High Street*

1  Eke Ernest
2  Smith Mrs M
3  Smith Mrs
4  Woodhouse Mrs
5  Franklin Mrs
6  Hall Mrs
7  Knowles Herbert
8  Bowman Mrs
9  Thorn Cecil

## ARTHUR STREET

*From 10 Windsor Terrace to*
*11 Wellington Street*

### North side

1  Proctor Fred
2  Fisher Robert
King's Lynn& District Working Men's Co-operative Society Ltd.  (bakery)
7  Dickinson Thomas
8  Scott William

### South side

5  Link George
6  Pitt George Albert
*here is Douro Street*

## ATBARA TERRACE

*From 30 Kitchener Street*

1  Elms William
2  Colby Arthur
3  Wells John
4  Addison Edward
5  Bedwell Walter
6  Pidgeon Thomas
7  Wells Jonn Macfarlane
8  Green Mrs
9  Riches George Henry
10  Cresey Thomas William

## ATTO'S PASSAGE
*From 82 Norfolk Street*

2 Johnson Mrs L
3a Shirley William

## ATTO'S YARD
*From 82 Norfolk Street*

1 Cooper Mrs R
2 Simpson Mrs
3 Davies Thomas William
4 Gathergood Fred
5 Stolham Mrs E
6 Williams Wilfred
7 —
8 —

## AUSTIN STREET
*From Chapel Street to 71 Norfolk Street*
*South-west side*

14 Terry John HW
14a Chilvers Thomas
16 Slater Mrs
18 Bowen Mrs
20 Cooper Arthur Edward
22 Carter Thomas Francis
24 Batterby Walter
26 Watkins Ambrose
28 Harwood Reginald James
30 Gant Mrs Annie (shopkeeper)
32 Bailey Frederick (window cleaner)
34 Gill Mrs
*here is Albert Street*
38 Pearman Mrs
40 Simpson Mrs
42 Bailey Albert Arthur
44 Grange Samuel
46 Benefer Charles Edward
48 Smith Thomas Edward
50 Bunting Frederick Robert
62 Currey Edmund
54 Smart Arthur
56 Rockett John Henry

58 Little William Henry
60 Hanwell Percy (ladies & gents tailors)
62 Baldry Leslie Ernest
64 Richmond Reginald James
*here is Hasting's Yard*
Hastings Mrs
Thurston John (coal merchant)
Thrower Stephen Arthur (general dealer)
———
66 Stebbings William
68 Holmes Mrs
*here is Thrower's Yard*
Anderson Alfred
———
70 Witting John G
72 Stinton Albert Victor
74 Greeves Harry
76 Riches William (chimney sweep)
78 Snare Jack
80 Walker Percy Edwin
82 Mayes Thomas
84 Williams George
*here is Hope Yard*
86 Winterton Joseph Daniel
88 Anderson James Amos
*here is Railway Passage*
90 Godfrey Mrs Harriet Sarah (shopkeeper)
92 Braithwaite Harry
100 Nurse Frederick Richard
102 Curry George John
104 Nicholls James Frederick
106 Gee Mrs
108 Senter Edward
Williams George (mineral water manufactory)
Scoon Scott (automobile engineer)
Dann George Frederick (boot repairer)
Kent George Andrew
North-east side
Rix & Groom Ltd. (coal merchants - yard)
131 Adams Leonard William
129 Francis Mrs

Atto's Yard, Norfolk Street 1934

| AUSTIN STREET (continued) | AVENUE ROAD |
|---|---|
| 127 Crowter Arthur W (electrician) | *From Ongar House, Tennyson Road* |
| 125 Juniper Samuel | North side |
| 123 Thompson Herbert | 1 — |
| 121 Furbank Thomas A & Son (undertakers) | 3 Duckworth William |
| King's Lynn & District Working Men's | 5 Lyon Frederick |
| Co-operative Society Ltd (model dairy) | 7 Rutter Walter Herbert |
| Midland & Great Northern Joint | 9 Waite Mrs |
| Railway (head offices) (RB Walker, | 11 Little Gerald Clyde David |
| traffic manager; WA Thomas, | 13 Sawyer William Y |
| stationmaster) | 15 Barnard James |
| Beaty GC & Sons (ships' smiths) | 17 Addie James |
| Eastern Roadways Ltd. (haulage | 19 Le Grice Ernest |
| contractors) | 21 Turner Frederick Robert |
| 23 Shaw H (nurseryman) | 23 Waldegrave Miss |
| Granger Miss F (Funchal) | 25 — |
| 15 Darrington William (fish merchant) | 27 — |
| *here is Chapel Lane* | 29 — |
| 9 Mrs Rose | 31 — |
| 7 Close Mrs | 33 Dishman Mrs |
| 5 Self John | *here is Park Avenue* |

| AVENUE ROAD (continued) | BACKHAM'S ALMSHOUSES |
|---|---|
| 35  Webster James George | *See Goodwins Road* |
| **South side** | |
| 8 — | **BAGGE'S YARD** |
| 10 Oldroyd Mrs E | *From 12 Nelson Street* |
| 12 Lewin John | 1  Drew Luke George |
| 14 Priest Louis | 2  Fenton Alfred |
| 16 Drew Frederick | 3  Clements James Henry |
| 18 Boud Frank | |
| 20 Hudson Charles | **BAKER LANE** |
| 22 Alexander Horace Charles | *From 103 High Street to 14 Queen Street* |
| 24 Holman James | **South side** |
| 26 Powell Horace B | 1  Davis Harry |
| 28 Bird George | 2  Griffen Mrs E |
| 30 Powell Misses | 3  Greeves John Steven & Sons  (smiths) |
| 32 Peake John William | Harrison & Scrimshaw  (gate makers) |
| 34 Morris Thomas R | 4  Barnaby Mrs E |
| 36 Drew Miss | 5  Howard Mrs F |
| 38 Hammond Misses AM & ES | Wright Jasper James  (baker) |

Baptists Yard, Broad Street on a late winter's afternoon in 1933.

21

Baxter's Plain looking towards the demolished Athenaeum, the site of the new General Post Office. To the left is the museum and to the right is Blackfriars Street.

### BAKER LANE (continued)
#### North side
Willey Francis & Co Ltd  (wool merchants)
Eagle Robert
Leake Henry & Son Ltd.  (oil cake manufacturers)  (King's Lynn Oil Mills)

### BANK BUILDINGS
*See Tuesday Market Place*

### BANK CHAMBERS
*See Tuesday Market Place*

### BAPTIST'S YARD
*From 24 Broad Street*
Sainty Frederick John  (chimney sweep)
Crome R & Sons  (heating engineers)

### BARDELL'S TERRACE
*See Saddlebow Road*

### BARDELL'S YARD
*From 30 Pilot Street*
2  Howard Alfred John
3  Backham Charles
4  Pegg Albert
5  —
6  Dye Charles Hammond
7  Greenwood Miss

### BATHS YARD
*From 21 Broad Street*
1  Curson George
2  —
3  Hooks Alfred
4  Seals Mrs EM
4a  Hornigold Albert
5  Barnes Charles

### BATTERBEE COURT
*From 20 Tower Street*

Baxter's Plain, looking towards the Majestic cinema and ballroom in 1937.

The foyer of the Majestic Cinema c1934.

## BAXTER'S PLAIN
*From Paradise Parade*
### South side
Post Office (C Gilchrist, postmaster)
*here is Blackfriars Street*
Reeve Ernest C (butcher)
Chilvers John James (watch maker)
Marsters Miss Vera  (ladies hairdresser)
*here is Tower Street*
### West side
*here is Broad Street*
Drew Miss Helen J  (milliner)
Fendley Miss Alice M  (confectioner)
*here is New Conduit Street*
Custance & Son (tailors)
Miles Frederick J  (chemist)
Hayden Misses F & E (ladies' hairdressers)
*here is Sedgeford Lane*

## BEDFORD STREET
*From 7 Marshall Street to 19 Stanley Street*
1  Loasby Donald
2  Fayers Thomas J
3  Hall Albert Thomas
4  Back Alfred
5  Palmer Albert
6  Sharpin George Walter
7  Reeve Alfred. William
8  Franklin Miss
9  Hooke Frederick William
10 Caley Mrs

## BEECH ROAD
*From Hardwick Road to Vancouver Road*
1  Younge Miss EM
2  Harris William S
3  Twiss Walter Percy
4  Fraser Richard
5  Watkins Alfred
6  Grummett Thomas
7  Isaacson Richard E
8  Gore Albert

9  Eastwick Mrs
10  Barratt John
11  Ferris Mrs
12  Haverson Cyril Thomas
14  Slipper David James
15  Smith Arthur
16  Addison Frederick
17  O'Dell Mrs
18  Crown Alfred Charles
19  Spencer Maurice
20  Oakley William
21  Goodale Richard
22  Ebling Jim Bryant
23  Reeve Mrs A
24  Friend George

## BEGLEY'S YARD
*From 2 Providence Street*
1  Leggett Mrs J
2  Fisher Mrs

Bennett's Yard

24

Bentinck Dock in the late 1930s. In the background is Bentinck Dock No.3 warehouse which had opened in 1898 - 15 years after the dock was first opened.

## BEGLEY'S YARD (continued)
3  Say Stanley
4  Rogers Mrs SJ

## BEGLEY'S YARD
*From 18 North Street*
   Petts Frank
8  Petts Thomas
7  Hornigold Samuel
   Castleton Charles
5  Gordon Edward
4  Eglinton George
3  Bone Ernest William
6  Castleton Archibald

## BEGLEY'S YARD
*From 67 Friars Street*
1  Winter Robert
2  Carter Mrs G
3  Foreman Robert William
4  Shorting Henry William

## BELL YARD
*From 99 Norfolk Street*

## BENNETT'S YARD
*From 18 Tower Street*
1  Benstead Richard
2  —
3  Norris James Henry

## BENTINCK DOCK
*From Estuary Road*
### North side
Chapman FE & Co Ltd. (timber merchants)
Bristow & Copley Ltd. (timber merchants)
Shell-Mex & B.P. Ltd
Stanton JT & Co. Ltd. (timber merchants)
### West side
Pure Cane Molasses Co. Ltd. (molasses refiners)

## BENTINCK STREET

*From 6 South Clough Lane to Russell Place*

### East side

1a English Frederick James
2a Beaty Francis
1 Peck Mrs E
2 Fayers Frederick Thomas
3 Elvin Mrs HE
4 Guy Walter J
5 Thompson William
6 Dixon George S  (tailor)

### West side

Burgess George  (Rose Cottage)
7 West Harry
8 Rowe Thomas
9 Lowthorpe Alfred
10 Lemmon William
11 —
12 —
13 —

## BEVIS WAY ♦

*From Marsh Lane*

Overton Harry Arthur (Aquata)
Booth William Arthur (Garfield)
Clinko John William (Sunnyside)
Moore Ernest Edward  (builder)
Reeve John Dawson
Hardy Mrs (Roseville)
Collison Gaston (builder) (Melbourne)
Leggett Albert (Montagu)
Fendley Walter  (Ivydene)

## BIRCHWOOD STREET

*From Hextable Road to 48 Loke Road*

### North side

1 Bath Harry  (boot maker)
2 Pearman Walter
3 Roper Bert
4 Taylor Frank
5 Hickman Arthur E
6 —

7 Bone Mrs
8 Pishorn Edward
9 Bush Walter
10 Plumley Mrs
11 Hardy Abel James
12 Pishorn Mrs
13 Goodson James
14 Mitson Alfred
15 Panton Robert
16 —
17 Parkes Walter
18 Walker Wilfred
19 Seaman Ernest
20 Girdlestone George
21 Brock William
22 Groom Arthur Charles
23 Ransom James
24 Goodson John
25 Gordon Leonard
26 Petts Frederick
27 Richardson Arthur
28 Smith John
29 Walker Mrs
30 Dixon Henry

### South side

31 Osborne Robert
32 Snelling Miss
33 Bloomfield James  (shopkeeper)
34 Manning William
35 Leman Albert Charles
36 Greeves Thomas
37 Scott Walter
38 Fish Charles
39 Whalen Walter
40 Whiley Henry
41 Lusher Henry
42 Spooner Jack
43 Hardy Frank
44 Wakefield John
45 Brittain James
46 Wharton Mrs
47 Anderson James

## BIRCHWOOD STREET (continued)

48 Hammond John
49 Rasberry Arthur
50 Senter John
51 Stapleton John Henry
52 Gant Mrs
53 Pitt Anthony
54 Scott Mrs
55 Balls Albert
56 Rake Alfred
    Rake Alfred  (shell fish merchant)

## BIRD'S YARD
*From 18 Pilot Street*

Bird's Yard, Pilot Street

## BIRDCAGE WALK
*From Carmelite Terrace to The Friars*
### North side
1 Baker Miss
2 Chilvers Robert
3 Hitchcock Stanley H
4 Fordham Miss A  (shopkeeper)
5 Barnaby William
6 Seakins Henry James
7 Bunn James
8 Sheldrick Mrs F

## BLACKFRIARS CHAMBERS
*See Blackfriars Street*

## BLACKFRIARS ROAD
*From 72 Norfolk Street to*
*St. John's Terrace*
### East side
*Frost's Buildings*
1 Overton Henry Edward
2 Slegg Delabear George
3 Skipper Miss

———

Bone JJ & Son  (builders)
Bone John J  (New House)
    *here is Paxton Terrace*
28 Chaliss Frederick G
27 Sibley Charles William
26 Bath Miss
25 Roper Mrs B  (grocer)
24 Barnes James  (jobmaster)
**Engineers' Tavern   (William Bowman)**
    *here is Coburg Street*
23 Coller R & Sons Ltd.  (coal merchants)
(offices & depot)
L&NER Railway Goods Depot
King s Lynn Station  L&NER and
M&GN Railway
M&GN Railway Goods Depot
Allworthy Reverend Edward James (vicar of St
John's Church)
St John the Evangelist's Church
### West side
la  Thrower Stephen A  (general smith)
1 Lubbock Arthur  (carman)
2 Flanders William
3 Peacock Hubert Reginald
4 Waldon Mrs
5 Howard Henry
6 Sooley George William
Brooke Bond & Co.  (tea warehouse)
7 Bone Miss
8 Taylor Mrs E
9 Ward James Minns
10 Playford Ernest Frederick

27

## BLACKFRIARS ROAD (continued)

11  Ashby Frederick George
12  East Victor Kenneth
13  Anderson Mrs Fanny  (newsagent)
Dawber, Townsley & Co. Ltd. (builders merchants)

*here is Wellesley Street*

Warner William A (Blackfriars House)
Gibson Mrs AL  (Bedford House)
Starr William John   (NSPCC inspector) (Malvern House)
Morison Mrs F (Douglas House)
16  Manning Mrs GA
LMS  Railway  Inquiry Office (WJ Bray, local agent)
Langford & Fidment   (tobacconists)
**Railway Hotel   (Samuel A Fuller)**

*here is Portland Street*

**The East Anglian Hotel  (Lillian Williams)**

**Grey Friars Tavern   (Frank H Withers)**

*here is Waterloo Street*


### BLACKFRIARS STREET
*From Baxter's Plain*
### West side

4  Bann John  senior
6  Bann John Samuel   (fish shop)
8  Owen Miss Miriam  (photographer)
8  Owen George
10  Wickham George C & Sons  (plumbers)
14  Rutland Sydney   (tobacconist)
16  Peck William  (dairyman)
18  Rose Mrs L
20  Tipple Richard S  (tailor)
22  Richardson Mrs
24  Staley Abraham J   (confectioner)
26  Bruce Lewis  (tailor)
28 —
30 & 32 Giles Bros  (motor engineers)
34  Eagleton William

36 Baker Mrs Elizabeth
37 Jackson Mrs
38 Rodgers George James S
42 Bart Walter  (shopkeeper)
44 Mitchell Frederick James
46 Pryor Fred  (hairdresser)
48 Cork Arthur  (baker)
50 Bocking William Arthur  (shopkeeper)
52 Fenemore Aubrey
54 Fayers Robert W & Sons  (builders)
56 Fysh Miss AM
58 McCulloch Alexander Ernest
60 Holman John William  (shopkeeper)
62 Carter Percy
64 Colls George
66 Eglen Walter
68 Countman William
70 Claxton Mrs
72 **Clough Fleet Tavern   (Alice Maud Greaves)**

*here is St. James' Road*
### East side
*here is private road leading to*
*Market Street & Paradise Parade*

1 **Princess Royal PH  (Mabel Annie Farrow)**
3 Eagle Willis
5 Palmer Miss
7 Divers F & Co.  (grocers)
9 Reader Horatio Maude
11 Dockerill Percy  (builder)
13 —

1936. Blackfriars Street view of demolition of the old Athenaeum, prior to the building of the new GPO. The new telephone exchange can be seen to the right of the picture.

### Blackfriars Chambers

Miles & Son  (auctioneers)
Miles SW  (land agent)

---

### Blackfriars Hall
### Stepney Baptist Church

15 Johnson Miss
17 Stevens Samuel & Son   (fishmongers)
*here is Railway Road*
Johnson William Henry  (saddler)
Large Miss Mary Ann  (greengrocer)
**Cozens Hotel   (Mrs EH Wanford)**
*here is St. John's Terrace*

### BLOTT'S YARD
*From 22 Purfleet Street*

### BOAL LANE
*From 4 Boal Street*
2  Capps William Edward
3 —
Kerner-Greenwood & Co. Ltd.
cement waterproofers (works)

### BOAL QUAY
*From Boal Street*
East Coast Steam Ship Co. Ltd
Paul R & W Ltd.  (cattle food manufacturers)
Marine Traders Ltd  (wharfingers)
LM&S  (Railway Harbour Office)
L&NER  (Railway Harbour Office)

### BOAL STREET
*From Bridge Street to Boal Quay*
North side
1  Thurlow Arthur
South side
2  Mitchell Thomas James R  (boot repairer)
2  Hewitt Matthew James
3  Sharpin Thomas
4  Scott William
Wells Albert Henry
*here is Boal Lane*

The corner of Bridge Street (left) and All Saints Street (right)

## BONE'S YARD
*From 32 Queen Street*

1  Harwood DH
2  Barrett William
3  Lovick George
4  Anderson George

## BREWERY BUILDINGS
*From 12 London Road*

1  Dickerson Mrs
2  Breeze Mrs M
3  Hensby Benjamin M
4  Starling Alfred
United Bowls Club  (AE Barker Hon. Sec.)

## BRICK YARD*
*From 47 Loke Road to Edma Street*
*here is Walker Street*
Irwin John

Pearman Frederick
Ward James R

## BRIDGE STREET
*From 18 All Saints Street to Church Street*
### East side

1a Scott Charles Edward
2a Kirby John
3a Lane Frederick George
4a Ringwood Mrs
5a Pearman Thomas
6a Witt Frederick
7a Crowe Arthur
8a Gamble Mathew
9a Waterman Alec
        *here is Miller's Court*
10  Thorn Mrs Sarah A  (baker)
11  Starling TJ   (fried fish dealer)
12  Davy Harry
        *here is Law's Yard*

## BRIDGE STREET (continued)

13 Smith Frederick  (shopkeeper)

*here is Crooked Lane*

8 Fiske Leonard James

8 Starling Mrs C   (general dealer)

7 Brindle Mrs

6 Lewis Mrs E

5 Youngs Mrs A

4 Coe Mrs EC  (shopkeeper)

3 Bullock Arthur Albert

2 Marsland Bertram

### Lady Bridge House

Liverpool Victoria Friendly Society

Commercial Union Assurance Co.

Witt Miss HM

———

### West side

*here is Boal Street*

23 **Ship Inn   (Herbert W Crake)**

Lewis Mrs Ethelburga  (baker)

Greenland Fishery Museum

(Mrs Ethelburga Lewis, curator)

29 Williamson Robert

30 Fiske Cecil Arthur

31 Barnes William Edward

32 Marshall Sydney

33 Neave Mrs

34 Hudson Mrs

35 Nuccoll Thomas S

36 Harbour Mrs H   (shopkeeper)

37 Macey Edward Arthur

38 **Hulk Inn   (Herbert George Mitchell)**

### BROAD STREET

*From Baxter's Plain to 13 Norfolk Street*

### East side

1 Eastman's Ltd.  (butchers)

2 Medlock Herbert R  (confectioner)

3 —

4 Hodgson Edward   (fried fish shop)

5 Drew Frederick  (boot repairer)

6 & 12 Trail Henry  (scale maker)

7 Nelson Joseph   (watch repairer)

*here is Softly's Yard*

8 Griffin George S   (greengrocer)

9 Chilvers Jacob Y  (boot repairer)

10 Fuller John   (shopkeeper)

10 Turner William

11 Jacobs Mrs Minnie M  (confectioner)

12 Reed Albert Edward   (newsagent)

12 Keen Walter N  (sign writer)

12 & 6 Trail Henry  (scale maker)

### Cattle Market

13 Finkelblach Myer  (watch repairer)

14 Crosskill Miss Ida   (confectioner)

King's Lynn Electric Theatre (Union

Cinema Co Ltd) (R Horobin, manager)

15 King William Henry

16 Reid Mrs Francesco  (wardrobe dealer)

Catleughs' of Lynn  (tailors)

### West side

Norfolk & Norwich Savings Bank

Slator John William & Sons  (ironmongers)

Sexton Bros   (fruit merchants)

37 Hilton Eric  (wireless engineer)

36 Giles Miss

35 Peckover Mrs N  (pork butcher)

34 Marsters CW Ltd.   (seedsmen)

33 Loasby George Frederick

Norfolk Regiment (TA) (5th battn) (B Co.)

Capt. C P Wood  (officer commanding)

30 **City of Norwich PH   (William E Harrod)**

29 Wilson James  (taxidermist)

28 Steward-Brown FM  (draper)

28a Smith William James  (herbalist)

27 & 26 Barnaby George & Son  (fishmongers)

25 Ewen Mrs AM  (cycle agent)

24 **Cattle Market Tavern  (Edward Goodson)**

*here is Baptist's Yard*

23 Hardy Mrs HM  (confectioner)

22 Thrower Mrs Violet   (shopkeeper)

21 Thrower Charles S  (hairdresser)

*here is Baths Yard*

Furbank Thomas A & Son  (undertakers)

Catleughs on the corner of Broad Street and Norfolk Street 1937.

## BROAD STREET (continued)
Lock William & Son Ltd.  (builders)
20 Southgate George Thomas
19 Wetherell Arthur
18 & 18a Sharpin William M  (greengrocer)

## BROADWAY
*From 21 Kirby Street*
1 Barley Walter
2 Jary Thomas
3 Cozens Arthur

## BROUGHTON COTTAGES
*From 43 Checker Street*
1 Dunkley Ernest
2 Sutton Mrs

## BROWN'S YARD
*From 16 St. James' Street*
1 Calcott John
2 Eagle Mrs A

3 Irwin Charles

## BROWNING'S YARD
*From 107 Norfolk Street*
1 Rudd Mrs
2 Woodward Ernest Henry
3 Rudd John Alex
4 Price Sidney
5 Hardy Thomas
6 Fox John
7 Ward Robert

## BUNNETT AVENUE
*From 79 Wisbech Road to*
*62 Saddlebow Road*
South side
2 Manning Frederick B
4 Rippengill  Martin
6 Guy Joseph Henry
8 Green Walter
10  Twite James

32

**R. CROME & SONS**

(H. C. & J. D. CROME)

## Heating Engineers

Acetylene Welding

Coppersmiths       Smiths-in-General

FENCING OF EVERY DESCRIPTION MADE TO ORDER

## BROAD ST., KING'S LYNN

Telephone 2437

### BUNNETT AVENUE (continued)

12  Crake Alex
14  Huggins Alfred
16  Osborne Frederick
18  Smith Harry
20  Yates Percy William
22  Thurston Walter HA
24  Ramm Wilfrid L
26  Wilson John Thomas
28  Branford William H
30  Jackman Albert E
32  Futter Samuel James
34  Green Arthur Francis
36  Watson Walter
38  Sharpin Walter
40  Higham Robert
42  Rodwell Robert Henry
44  Lawrence Frederick
46  Brock Elijah H
48  Simpson Joseph Henry
50  Wilson Thomas
52  Eagle Frederick
54  Warner Sydney Charles
56  Fenn Henry William

### North side

1  Oakes Arthur
3  Witt Albert Edward
5  Peake Robert C
7  Rose William
9  Sedgwick Joseph
11  Edgley George

13  Colby Cyril
15  Collison Cyril
17  Hooks William
19  Skipper John William
21  Sainty Arthur George
23  Barker Horace
25  Barber Baden
27  Watson George Alfred
29  Luscombe Henry
31  Watts Mrs
33  Harrop John Edward
35  Lloyd Edward
37  Shorter Dudley
39  Gray Thomas
41  Arrowsmith Matthew
43  Chase Samuel
45  Crake Percy V
47  Riches Claude
49  Yates William
51  Bird Ernest

### BURKITT STREET

*From 31 Loke Road*

### West side

1  Latchford Richard
2  Wright Stanley Charles
3  Wright Arthur Ernest
4  Starling John
5  Moy Sidney
6  Harris Thomas Edward
7  Fisher Edward Charles
8  Lawson Mrs
9  Thompson William
10  Scott Jack
11  Lawson William
12  Bugg Fernley George  (shopkeeper)
13  Howard James
14  Chesson Edward

*here is Walker Street*

Gamble William (Lorn House)
Bates Ernest (Welbeck)
Butcher William Edward (Solway)

Celebrations at the back of Burkitt Street in 1935. George V Silver Jubilee.

## BURKITT STREET (continued)

Butcher William (Medway)
Dexter Henry (Galway)
Giles Walter. (Milton House)
Brock Mrs (Rosedale House)
Bull Samuel (Swiss Cottage)
Jackson Robert William (Belgium Cottage)
Thurston Robert  (dairyman)
(Norfolk View)
Jex Horace Albert (Locarno)
Jex Albert Victor (Geneva)

### East side

Ess Arthur (Homeland)
Groom Frank (Fern Cottage)
Wakefield Henry (Rose Cottage)
Thompson Frederick (Alford Cottage)
8a Ollett Thomas
7a Pickett Albert J
6a Jaggs Phillip
6a Spooner Mrs
Cook Harry (Albion Cottage)

Chase John William (Ellen Cottage)
Hornigold Charles (Violet Cottage)
Bridges Lazarus (Lily Cottage)
*here is Walker Street*
Hornigold William (Pretoria)
Stanford Robert (Hickling House)
Ayre Mrs (Craigside)
Ridley Mrs (Ivy Cottage)
Baxter Frederick (Victoria House)
Bone Ernest (Grace Darling House)
Fisher William (Valerian)

## BURTON'S COURT*
*From 5 New Conduit Street*

2  Fox Leslie
3  Murray William Clark
5  Woodhouse Mrs MA
6  Simpson Stanley William

## CALIFORNIA YARD*
*From 104 Norfolk Street*

2  Blyth Mrs
3  Baker Charles Thomas J
4  Hare Richard
5  Haverson Mrs
6  Thurston George
7  Haverson Frederick P
8  Eastwood Mrs
9  Catchpole Thomas
10  Green Albert
11  Hare Mrs E

## CARMELITE TERRACE
*From South Lynn Plain to The Friars*
### South side

1  Bone Robert  (builder)
2  Thompson Mrs
3  Dyble Mrs
4  Whitehand Frederick
5  Lewis Mrs
6  Thrower Frederick Walter

## CARMELITE TERRACE (continued)

7 Bartram John Henry
8 Chamberlain John B
9 Bond Ernest Abraham
10 Crane Horace John
11 Haigh Stanley
12 Greeves Ernest James
13 Townsend William C
14 Wright Herbert
15 Sturman Basil Oscar
16 Reed Herbert
17 Troman Oscar Leslie
18 Hitch George

## CATTLE MARKET

*See Paradise Parade*

## CHADWICK STREET

*From 14 Providence Street*

### South-east side

2 Purchase Mrs
3 Jackson Albert James
4 Stratton Stanley George
5 Barrett James William (tailor)
6 Lee Mrs
7 Warner Ambrose

### North side

8 Whomes Herbert Arthur
9 Ashby John William
10 Pidgeon Thomas Henry
11 Reynolds William
12 Colquhoun Duncan
13 Patten John Thomas
14 Shepperson Mrs
15 Goodale Mrs SE

## CHAPEL BUILDINGS

*See Chapel Street*

## CHAPEL COTTAGES♦

*See Gayton Road*

## CHAPEL LANE

*From 34 Austin Street to 6 Pilot Street*

### West side

1 Rose Mrs Martha
2 Belcham Miss
3 Mitchelson Ernest senior
4 Mitchelson Ernest junior
5 Senter Thomas William
6 Booth Robert
7 Bunting James
8 Bailey Robert John

## CHAPEL STREET

*From 133 Norfolk Street to St. Ann's Street*

### East side

5 Riches William Charles (shopkeeper)
6 —
7 Woollard George  (butcher)
 *here is Miles's Square*
8 Naylor Walter  (shopkeeper)
9 Hunter Arthur  (boot repairer)
10 Gamble Henry
11 Foreman Miss Louisa  (shopkeeper)
12 Minster Percy
**Black Horse PH  (Harry John H Rowley)**
Partridge & Forster  (solicitors)
Hunstanton Pier Co. (FGW Hayes, sec.)
Gargett Edgar  (St. Augustine's)
 *here is Austin Street*
**Raynham House**
Ridsdale Miss
Webb Miss Blanche (nurse)
Meneeley Miss Mary Grace  (nurse)
———
2 Simon Robert

### West side

14 Johnson Samuel
15 Fox William
16 Stokoe George  (draper)
17 Ely Samuel David  (greengrocer)
18 Hemeter John
19 & 20 Sayer James George  (baker)

## CHAPEL STREET (continued)

21 Goodson Henry Samuel
22 Earl Andrew John
23a Winlove Claude

In 1936 the Tuesday Market saw the erection of 31 new pig-pens.

24  Ward Mrs
*here is Ravenshaw's Yard*
25 Fox George Leslie

### Chapel Buildings
1  Semon Albert Victor
2  Daisley Edward

---

26 Howlett William  (chimney sweep)
27 Oakes George W  (verger of St. Nicholas Church)
*here is Market Lane*
31 Hayes & Sons  (decorators))
   Donaldson Alex   (fish merchant)
   Bracey & Wells   (pork butcher)
   Manning Alfred   (hairdresser)
*here is Surrey Street*
32  Harrowing Robert  (dairy)
34  Salt Harry
36 Cook John Edward & Son  (butchers)
37 Brooke William Maurice  (baker)
38 Towler Robert  (hairdresser)

## CHAPEL YARD
*From 11 St Ann's Street*
1  Holden James Christmas

2  Gent Mrs
3  Hansell Albert Ernest
4  Cook Mrs
5  Bailey Mrs

## CHARLES STREET
*From 43 Guanock Terrace to*
*William Street*
2  Nicholls Walter. William
3  Smith Hubbard Charles

## CHASE AVENUE
*From York Road to Sidney Street*
1 Rose George Albert
3 Burges Miss M
5 Smith James Arthur
7 Massingham Albert E
9 Smith Mrs Ruth
11 Barker Rev. John  (Wesleyan)
13 Reid Rupert Douglas H
*here is Vancouver Avenue*
15 King Albert E  (insurance agent)
17 Gore Albert Edward
19 Raines Albert
21 West Robert
23 Smith Horace James  (insurance agent)
25 —
27 Suggett Arthur
29 Setchell Arthur William
31 Howlett Ernest Wilson
33 Bird Harry
35 Howard Henry Percy
37 Slater Sidney C
39 Nicholson Albert N
41 Metcalf Arnold
43 Orviss Fred

## CHASE COTTAGES
*See Thomas Street*

## CHECKER STREET

*From 77 London Road to 41 Friars Street*

### West side

1 Drew George
3 Grief Mrs
5 Petts Mrs
7 Kirby Youngs Potter
9 Crake Ernest
11 —
13 Plain Frederick Ernest
15 Clarke Benjamin John
17 Prior George R
19 Reed George Frederick
*here is Spencer's Square*
21 Waymark HS (grocer)
23 Playford George
25 Fysh Mrs
27 Tyler Arthur Henry
29 Leverington George
31 Baxter Mrs H
31a Leverett Mrs S
33 Lusher Frederick
35 Fox Mrs M
*here is Evett's Yard*
Williamson James (Lime House)
*here are Broughton Cottages*
43 Williamson Walter William
45 —
47 Rodwell Edward John
49 Hammond John T
51 Green Arthur
53 Sennett Thomas M
55 Daisley Frederick
57 Daisley Frederick Joseph

### East side

*here is Chesson's Yard*
2 Riches Walter
4 Neal Edward
6 Neal Herbert F
8 Smart Albert
10 Linwood Joseph Thomas
12 Lovell John

Chapel Yard

14 Dent Alfred
16 Thompson George William
18 Bloom Charles Frederick
20 Earl Herbert
22 Gathercole Mrs
24 Simpson Thomas R
26 Mitchell Alfred
28 Beevis Albert
30 Oakes William Walter
32 Emerson Hubert M
34 Walker Sydney Victor
36 Bunfield Miss
38 Hendry James
40 Broad Mrs
42 Jones Miss FM
44 Baker J Royal
46 Snelling Herbert Jonathan
48 Lee John
50 Greenwood William
52 Turner Mrs

Church Street looking south. The corner of St Margaret's Church can just be seen on the right.

## CHECKER STREET (continued)

54  Younge William Charles
56  Langley William Edward
58  Fox Thomas
60  Rudd Thomas Henry
62  Castle Mrs E
64  Towler Mrs R
66  Jarvis Edward Wright
68 & 70  **Bowling Green Inn  (William Ernest Collison)**
72  Crowe Thomas
74  Thompson Mrs
76  Selwood Mrs

## CHESSON'S YARD
*From 2 Checker Street*
1  Jubey Mrs

## CHURCH COTTAGES
*See Gayton Road*

## CHURCH LANE
*From 1 All Saints Street*
### South side
1  Blackburn Frederick
2  Mitchell Robert William
3  Wicks Arthur
9  Haycock Herbert Edward
### North side

*here is Lowe's Yard*
5  Barnard Bertie James
6  Fiddaman Alfred
Roman Catholic School (mixed)
All Saints' Church

## CHURCH STREET
*From St James' Street*
### East side
1  Bocking Mrs Caroline  (shopkeeper)
2  Gorbould George William
3  Popkis John Hall
Gorbould Bros.  (motor engineers)
8  Roy's Advertising Station
8  Redington Stewart Robert
*here is Payne's Court*
10  Grimes Ernest Alfred
Johnson  W H & Sons Ltd. (motor works)
**Three Tuns PH  (John Tuffs)**
11  Ess Arthur  (tobacconist)
12  Baker William  (greengrocer)
### West side
15  Mallett Frederick  (decorator)
16  Connelly Miss Elizabeth  (dressmaker)
17  Wright William L  (grocer)
18  Nicholls Brothers  (fishmongers)
19  Hunter Mrs Edith  (shopkeeper)
*here is Priory Lane*
20 & 21  Rose Mrs Ruth  (grocer)
22  Smith Mrs ME
Lynn Workers' Club Craftsmen's Guild Ltd (Herbert Pinnington, president)
26  Allen Misses  (dressmakers)
27  Barrett Thomas
*here is Linay's Yard*
29  Simper John
George Alfred Henry  (pork butcher)

## CHURCHMAN'S YARD
*From 27 North Street*
Watts Reginald
Colby Mrs

Church Street looking towards Bridge Street, at the junction with Stonegate Street. The shop on the corner is 1, Church Street. It is owned by Mrs Caroline Bocking.

## COBURG STREET

*From 24 Blackfriars Road to*
*12 Wyatt Street*

### North side

2  Reeve Charles
3  Pollyn Bertie
4  Simpson Mrs AM
5  Barr John Thomas
        *here is Reid Street*
6  Ames William
7  Pinnington Herbert
8  Sheen Henry Edward
9  Mitchley Thomas
10  Gunns Frederick, James
11  Gribble William
        *here is Dilke Street*
12  Marshall Miss
13  Bailey Edward

14  Easton Atheling Edgar
14a  Beaty Mrs Harriett   (general shop)
15  Clark Miss
16  Hammond Miss
17  Mott Ernest

## COLBY'S YARD

*From 12 Providence Street*

4  Scott James Henry
5  Watson George William
6  Catton Albert Edward
7  Reeve George William
9 Leggett Mrs S

## COMMON STAITH QUAY

*From Ferry Street*

Ouse Traders Ltd.   (pickle manufacturers)
North Sea Steamship Co Ltd

Marine Traders Ltd   (warehousemen)
**COMMON STAITH QUAY (continued)**
Meters Office   (WH Baxter, head meter)
Harbour Master's Office   (Capt. AE Holmes, harbour master)
King's Lynn Conservancy Board
Fire Engine Station   (JW Shaw, captain)

### CORN EXCHANGE
*See Tuesday Market Place*

### CORNWELL TERRACE
*See Saddlebow Road*

### CORONATION SQUARE
*From Greyfriars Road to Union Street*
1   Harpley Mrs R
2   Shirley Fred
3   Smith Mrs EK
4   Smith Miss
5   Gurney George
6   Eagle Mrs
7   Howard Charles Isaac
8   Howard William Edwin
9   Hughes Stanley
10   Bell William James
11   Langridge Alfred George
12   Oakes George Frederick
13   Shearman Mrs IJ
13a Arnop Arthur
14   Nicholson A Wilfred
15   Unwin John James
16   Harpley George William
17   Turvey Robert James
18   Pole Mrs
19   Hammond Mrs
20   Haverson Thomas
21   Witley Mrs E
        *here are Providence & Union Streets*
22   Akers Thomas William Bradshaw
23   Crowe Bertie Frederick  (fishmonger)
        *here is Crooked Lane*

24 Cage William   (shopkeeper)
24 Skelleter James
25 Myers Harry
25 Myers Mrs Ethel  (teacher of piano)
26 Blench Mrs SA  (boarding house)
27 Green Gerald Dover Thomas
King's Lynn Christian Science Hall

### COUNCIL HOUSES
*See Saddlebow Road*

### COUNTY COURT ROAD
*From London Road to Street James' Place*
North side
Primitive Methodist Church Hall
**Royal Standard PH   (John E Medlock)**

### CRANFIELD'S WHARF
*See Wellesley Street*

### CRESSWELL STREET
*From 21 Loke Road*
East side
2   —
3   Bartram Mrs L  (shopkeeper)
4   Shafto Frederick
5   Brock George William
6   Massingham Mrs
7   Marsters James
8   Jex Frederick
9   Cook Frederick
10   Cook Harry   (shell fish merchant)
11   Barnes Frederick William
12   Valentine Miss KM (teacher of music)
12   Valentine William
13   Holland Mrs
14   Paddy Thomas
15   Guy John
16   Cook Arthur  (shopkeeper)
        *here is Walker Street*
17   Anderson Harry
18   Anderson John Thomas

19  Lubbock William Charles

**CRESSWELL STREET (continued)**

20  Wheatley Arthur Edward
21  Ellis Henry Robert
22  Bone James
23  Bone Edward
24  Scott Robert
25  Goodwin William
26  Groom William J
27  Parfrement Ernest Albert
28  Cook John Spilman
29  Powditch Thomas
29a Griffin Frederick Charles
30  Hancock Albert Edward
30a Allen John Joseph Alfred
31  Thurston Michael
31a Bone George Charles
32  Gore Frederick
32a Barker George William
Smith William (Woodcote)

### West side

Lemmon Sidney (Sidwin)
33a Barker John
34  Barker Sydney James
35  Clarke Leonard James
36  Taylor Mrs
37  Barron Mrs
38  Bone William
39  Petts Sidney
40  Twaite Mrs
41  Lake Frederick
42  Chase William
43  White Mrs
44  Mitchley Mrs
45  Collins Mrs
46  Pratt Sydney
47  Watts Albert
48  Scott Mrs
49  Cresey John
50  Delahoy Matthew G
51  Raines Thomas
52  Grange Frederick

*here is Walker Street*

53  —
54  —
55  Flowers EF
56  Goodson Sydney
57  Davis William
58  Bayes John Henry
59  Pratt Alfred Lewis
60  Case Victor Frederick
61  Watts Thomas
62  Cresey George
63  Dixon Harry
64  Petts Walter James
65  Goodson Harry James
66  Wood Henry James
67  Hall P & V  (upholsterers)
68  Petts Frederick

### CRISP'S YARD

*From 8 Stonegate Street*

1  Dixon Albert Edward
2  Fisk Leonard James
3  Hall Percy

### CROME'S YARD

*From 7 Union Place*

1  Main Frank
2  Griffiths Mrs
3  Ellis Bert
4  Eglen Richard

### CROMWELL TERRACE

*From Southgate Street to*
*28 Friar's Street*

### South-west side

1  Sutton John  (boot repairer)
2  Curtis Richard AF
3  Hall Mrs
4  Riches John William
5  Skerry Mrs Martha

Crooked Lane looking towards Bridge Street in 1933.

## CROOKED LANE
*From 8 Bridge Street to*
*23 Coronation Square*
### South side
2  Eastwood John William
3  Russell Frederick
4  —
5  Brightwell Henry Charles
6  Crow Mrs MJ
7  —
8  Whiley Walter Richard
9  Needham Alfred
*here is Union Place*
### North side
1  Green John
2a Woodhouse Edward S

## CROSS LANE
*From 16 Sedgeford Lane to Union Lane*
1  Greeves Mrs IM

7  Holmes Richard
8  Green George
9  Reed James Arthur
10  Collier William M
12  Twite William James
13  Walker Albert
*here is Watson's Yard*

## CROSS YARD
*From 5 Littleport Street*
### West side
1  —
2  —
3  —
4  —
5  —

## DAISLEY'S BUILDINGS
*From 2 Providence Street*
1  Harper Mrs
2  Farrow Robert William

42

## DAISLEY'S BUILDINGS (continued)

3 Say Frederick William
4 Benefer William Edward
5 Long William
6 Cooper Mrs Emma
7 Dyble Allan
8 Lyon Mrs A
9 Oakes Josiah Hart
10 White George Alfred
11 Hayes Thomas Green
12 Allen George
13 —
14 Turnbull Stanley
15 Hornsby Charles
16 Reeve Mrs

## DEVONSHIRE'S YARD*
*20 North Street*

2 Ashby Walter Nesbit
3 Pamment Arthur
4 Benefer George
5 Benefer John
6 Colby Arthur
8 Wheeler Arthur Henry
9 Collis Mrs

Devonshire's Yard 1933.

## DIAMOND STREET
*From Wisbech Road*

### East side

1 Crome James Arthur
3 Mummery Leslie Leopold
5 Fox Percy
7 Humphrey Arthur C
9 Leggett Harry
11 Allen Francis ST  (slater)
13 Simpson Robert
15 Watson Rupert Robert
17 Fitheridge Ernest
19 Coston John Hodgson
21 Jackson Edwin Thornton
23 Scott Edward
25 Cobbold Edward Francis

27 Bunnett Robert   JP
29 Pickett Archibald
31 Fayers Robert Henry
33 Godfrey Frederick
35 Catton Thomas
37 Kirman Frederick
39 Rockett Charles
41 Smith Louis Ernest

### West side

2 De Peare Mrs
4 Lake Thomas
6 Curson Robert Anthony
8 Hides Daniel Edmund
10 Clitheroe George

Cross Yard, looking towards Littleport Street.

| **DIAMOND STREET (continued)** | 22 Riches John Edward |
|---|---|
| 12 Hammond Mrs ME | 24 Reddy John |
| 14 Tyler Mrs E | 26 Fisher Frederick Ernest |
| 16 Croot Albert | 28 Todd Elijah |
| 18 Burrows Thomas | 30 Link Mrs G |
| 20 — | 32 Mann Walter |

Daisley's Buildings (Providence Street) 1933

## DIAMOND STREET (continued)

34 Christian Frederick
36 Wakefield John
38 Clitheroe George William
40 Simpson William
42 Jarvis Herbert

## DIAMOND TERRACE
*From Diamond Street*

1 King's Lynn & District Working
Men's Co-operative Society Ltd
2 Howling Mrs
3 Jary Mrs
4 Patterson Mrs S
6 Dawson George Herbert
6 Walker John William

## DILKE STREET
*From 11 Coburg Street*
### West side

1 Meggett Joseph S
2 Mann James E
3 Rayner Miss
4 Grief John
5 Fletcher Richard
6 Simpson William
7 Chilvers Mrs M
### North side
8 Waterfield Harry
### East side
9 Valentine Augustus
10 Bonney Leonard
11 Eastwick Miss
12 Clark Stanley Cyril
14 Everett Wilfred A
14a Eglen Frederick
15 Starling James

**DONOVAN YARD**

*See Littleport Street*

**DOUBLE ROW**

*From 45 Front Row*

### South side

1 Ransom Thomas Alfred
2 —
3 Ewing John
4 Waudby Mrs
5 Fenley Mrs
6 Holmes Ernest
7 Brady James
8 Kent Henry
9 Bowman Reuben
10 Cripps Mrs
11 Tilson Ernest William
12 Bentley William Thomas
13 Ransom Mrs
14 Jerry Walter Cecil
15 Shipp Edward
16 Fossett Walter
17 Girdlestone Frederick John
18 Asker Arthur
19 —
20 Cozens Robert
20a Adcock Stanley
   Langley Harry  (dairyman)

### North side

21 Bagge Walter
22 Gamble Frederick
23 Empson Sidney Alfred  (shopkeeper)
24 Back Charles
23 Reynolds Henry
26 Fisher Mrs
27 Long Mrs
28 Watson Albert
29 Sharman Henry Ernest
30 Hammond Mrs
31 Horsley William
32 Hannam Norman
33 Bowman George

34 Squirell George
35 Wagg Alfred Henry
**Highgate Mission Hall**
37 Reed Thomas Walter
38 King Archie Edgar

**DOURO STREET**

*From 49 Windsor Road to 6 Arthur Street*

### East side

1 Boud Frank
2 Skedge Mrs
3 Ward Ernest
4 Patterson Frederick
5 Barnaby Wilfred
6 Tungate James
7 Drew Ernest
8 Sanderson James

### West side

9 Whittaker Percy William
10 Willis Reginald
11 Belcham Miss
12 Cook John
12a Woodward Ernest Harry
14 Finney John Saville
15 Bushell Alfred E
16 Newman Charles

**EAST PLACE**

*See East Street*

**EAST STREET**

*From 21 Albert Street*

1 Carter Tom
2 Rayner William
3 Folker Edward
4 Griffin Jabez
5 Shread John William
   Pyshorn James Walter
6 Gent Mrs
7 Massingham Robert
8 Goodings William
9 Barr John William

Silver Jubilee celebrations of King George V in Highgate Double Row in 1935.

### East Place (EAST STREET)

1 West George
2 Borrmann Herrmann
3 Cook James

### EAST ANGLIA PLACE
### (formerly Edwards Yard)
*From 5 Providence Street*

2 Matchett Albert
5 Ess Albert Edward
6 Driver Mrs
7 Ansell Frederick
8 Toll Frederick
9 Youngs Sydney
10 Batterby Mrs
11 Bloom Mrs J
12 Drew Mrs SA
13 Williamson Walter Ernest
14 Lake Jack

### EASTGATE STREET
*From 17 Gaywood Road*
East side

1 Lake John T
2 Betts Charles William
3 Gibson Richard
4 Gibson William
5 Jackson George
6 Beaumont Jesse
7 Massey Arthur
8 Sewell William
9 Carter Ernest
10 Riches Robert
11 Jacobs Harry
12 Gee William
13 Cave Herbert
14 Laws John WF
15 Banyard Robert George
16 Hipkin William
17 Green Mrs
18 Link Albert
19 Fake Alfred
20 Simpson Richard

West side
*here is Archdale Street*

East Anglia Place, Providence Street c1934

## EDMA STREET
*From 105 Loke Road (extension)*
*to Salters Road*
### North side
1  Bone Samuel
2  Youngs William Charles
### South side
3  Pratt Frederick
4  Moore Charles D
5  Manning Percy
6  Rose Mrs
7  Mitchley Thomas
8  Blyth John Henry

## EDWARD STREET
*From Robert Street*
### South side
1  Pooley John William
2  Curzons Oliver
3  Allen Miss
4  Skerritt Matthew
5  Crisp Sidney
6  Holman Joseph Edward
### North side
7  Robotham Mrs SM
8  Barker Edward John
9  Huddlestone Thomas Henry
10 Stebings Walter
11  West Frederick Harry
12  Wollard Frederick George William
13  Clarke William Allan

### EDWARD'S YARD*
*From 2 Market Lane*
1  Norris William
2  Whitfield James
   Clover Harry

### ESTUARY ROAD
*From Pilot Street*
*here is Hextable Road*
Primitive Methodist Chapel
**Victoria PH   (Minnie Backham)**
*here is Loke Road*
Savages Ltd.  (motor engineers)
Brown Adam  (Estuary House)
*here are Bentinck Dock & railway crossing*
Anglo-American Oil Co. Ltd
Shell-Hex & B.P. Ltd

### ETHEL TERRACE
*From 28 Friars Street*
#### South-east side
1  Haylett Mrs
2  Curtis Arthur
3  Paige William Bennett
4  Skerry Alfred A
5  Little William
6  Woomes John Thomas

### EVETT'S YARD
*From 37 Checker Street*
1 —
2 —
3 —
4 —

### EXHIBITION TERRACE
*From 31 Front Row Highgate*
1  Smith John Robert
2  Thurston John
3  Payne Alfred
4  Drew George Henry
5  Marshall John Ernest

6  Ellis Arthur

### EXLEY'S YARD
*From 7 Purfleet Street*

### EXTON'S PLACE
*continuation of Exton's Road*
#### North side
1  Harrod Robert William
2  Edge George Albert
3  Granger Frederick  (shopkeeper)
4  Green Robert Matthew
5  Greeves Arthur
6  Burton Percy George
#### South side
Coston Mrs C E   (Victoria House)
2a Feltwell Joseph
3a Perry James William
4a Banton John Charles
*here is King's Avenue*
7  Greeves Mrs
8  Stolham Robert
9  Vearncombe Ernest
10  Wickham Streader Charles
11  Eales Arthur

### EXTON'S ROAD
*From Windsor Terrace to 1 Exton's Place*
#### North side
1 Rolfe Edward Frederick
2 **Seven Sisters PH   (John William Kent)**
*here is Aberdeen Street*
3  Bocking Frederick Henry  (bricklayer)
4  Wyatt Miss
5  Beales Miss
6  Drew Stanley
7  Ollett Ernest William
8  Moore Mrs
9  Stoakley Alfred
10 Steggles Frederick Cecil
*here is Peel Street*
11  Dines Wilfrid C

49

## EXTON'S ROAD (continued)

12  Bullen William
13  Taylor Arthur
14  Violen Daniel
15  Green Henry
16  Hancock George Robert
Brown Henry Charles  PhD  (Yoxford House)
*here is Tennyson Road*
Scale William Ford (Thorne Lea)
Pattrick Mrs (Exton lodge)
36  King's Lynn Institution  (M Illingworth
master, Mrs Illingworth matron)
Winlove-Smith Mrs (Wyngosee)
Brown Joseph S (Dereham Cottage)

### South side

Dawson John (Ivy Cottage)
*here is Holcombe Avenue*
Bootman Frederick Charles (The Lodge)
*here is Goodwins Road*

### Haylett Terrace

1  Bruce Reginald Ernest
2  Towler Robert William
3  Fawcett Edward   (builder)
4  Smith George Henry

17  Dudgeon Miss Ethel
19  Thompson Amos
20  Holt Thomas
21  Aveis William Albert
21a Baker William Franklin
*here is Graham Street*
22  Jones William George
23  Smith Charles
24  Dunbabin Mrs E
25  Drew James Henry
26  Petchell William
27  Dye Mrs
*here is Russell Street*
28  Craske Frederick  (baker)
29  Tawn John
30  Bugg Henry

## FACTORY AVENUE
*From Saddlebow Road*

Trinder Richard T  (Cantley Lodge)
Thijs William  (Wind Hock)
Smith B  (Whitehall)
Thijs WJH

## FARROWS BUILDINGS*
*From 45 Lynn Road*

2  Shipp Creek
3  Mitchley Herbert George
4  Allen Mrs
5  Alexander Leslie Alfred
6  Adcock Jermyn W
7  Elsegood Harry  (dairy)
8  Sizeland Frederick James
9  Bullock Samuel
10 Darnell Mrs

## FERMOY AVENUE
*From 5 Salters Road*

1  Back Horace William
2  Witt Sidney
3  French George H
4  Malt Alfred
5  Hardy George
6  Neal Samuel James
7  Backham Frederick
8  Smith Walter
9  Nurse Richard Frederick
10  Parr George
11  Neave Mrs
12  Leggett Charles

## FERRY LANE
*From 23 King Street*

1  Lemmon JE
2  Chapman Thomas William (greengrocer)
Barrett William (agent Hearts of Oak
Benefit Society)
Ouse Amateur Sailing Club (Eric Proctor, sec)

## FERRY STREET
*From Tuesday Market Place*
*to Common Staith Quay*
Hatton Harry
Dye Alfred Claxton (Birtle Dene)
Globe Hotel Garage
**Crown & Mitre PH   (Thomas W Rose)**

## FIELD LANE♦
*From Field Road*
1  Thompson Fred
2  Seaman Eric
3  Fakenbridge William
5  Lyones Arthur Leslie
6  Grange Edward John
7  Oughton George
8  Boucher Benjamin
10  Sparrow Frederick
11  Panks Percy
12  Thompson Wilfred Harry
Hawes George (Elsdene)

## FIELD ROAD♦
*From Gayton Road*
### East side
Clarke Albert Victor (Colville)
Hewitt John (Tre-lan)
Thompson Reginald (Sunningdale)
Twiddy Howard (Emlyn)
Chamberlain James (Sunset)
Colman Alfred. Herbert (Ramsdene)
Howard Arthur (Clovelly)
Twyman John CC (Heathcote)
Morley Rd. Taylor (St. Catherine)
Green Mrs (Meadowcroft)
Rowe Stanley (Ringstead)
Hutchins William
Harris Albert Wilfred
Hewett Walter (Evoco)
Anderson Ernest (Viern)
King's Lynn Gaywood Council School

### West side
1  Bensley Harry
2  Sizeland Walter K
3  Targett Mrs
4  Lusher Albert Edward
5  Akers Charles E
6  Madle Ernest F
Dodman David (The Oaks)

## FLEECE YARD
*From 55 Friars Street*
1  Clark Mrs
2  —
3  Green Robert
4  Bussey James
5  Gamble Mrs
6  Franklin Francis
7  Mitchell Alfred Ernest
8  Clare Albert John

## FREDERICK PLACE
*From 2 Valinger's Place*
### North side
1  Benefer Edward
2  Young John William
3  Starling Mrs
4  Dyble Samuel  senior
5  Dyble Samuel William J   junior
6  Howard Alfred James
### South side
7  Jenkinson Henry
8  Booer Sydney
9  Catton Mrs

## FRIARS (THE)
*From 20 All Saints Street*
Springall RF & Sons Ltd.  (timber merchants)
Fachney Alec J  (cabinet maker)
Worfolk & Sons  (boat builders)

## FRIARS PLACE
*From South Lynn Plain*

1 —
2 Simpson Walter Robert
3 Evans Mrs
4 —
5 —
6 —
7 McGibbon Mrs M

## FRIARS STREET
*From 5 South Lynn Plain*
*to 17 Southgate Street*
### East side

1 Long Walter
3 Sheen Sturgeon Harry
5 Stinton Stanley William
7 Clarke Henry Milson
9 Kerry Reginald
11 Curson James William
13 Merrywest George
     *here is Ploughwrights Yard*
17a Eke Ernest C
Flight William (Laurel House)
19 Norton Edward
21 Jackson Mrs S
23 Page Mrs AE (confectioner)
25 —

27 —
29 —
31 Ward Frederick John
33 Mott Mrs ME
35 South Sidney
37 Barrett Charles P
39 Gregory Mrs
41 Brown James
     *here is Checker Street*
43 Nunn Sidney Albert
45 —
47 Depear Leonard
49 Pratt Edward
51 Edgeley Frederick William
53 Gentle Charles Edward
55 Hornigold Mrs H   (shopkeeper)
     *here is Fleece Yard*
59 Deans A & Sons (shopkeepers)
61 Gray Ernest
63 Callaby Ernest
65 Haskett William Jesse
67 Marsters Percy
     *here is Begley's Yard*
69 & 71 Clarke & Son   (bakers)
73 Mitchell Mrs
75 Massingham Matthew
     *here is Kemble's Yard*

A new fleet of Bestyett delivery vehicles line up on the Friars in 1938

## FRIARS STREET (continued)

77 —
79 Ketteringham Mrs
81 Baxter Horace
83 Massen Mrs J

### West side

Elsden's Almshouses
*here are Whitefriars & Gladstone Roads*
2 Ward JW & Son  (lodging house)
2a Ashling Arthur
4 Addison Mrs
6 Bracebridge Arthur
8 Bailey John William
10 Manning-Coe Sidney
12 Thorne Mrs MAK
14 Catton Arthur
18 Smithson Edmund
20 Caston Charles William
22 Fulcher Leonard
Barwood George Henry   (sign writer)
*here are Whitefriars Cottages*
24 Oakes Arthur Edward (coal merchant)
26 Judd Herbert
28 Skipper Mrs
Giles & Bullen   (haulage contractors)
*here is Ethel Terrace*

## FRONT ROW

*From 2a Gaywood Road*

### West side

Cullen Arthur Richard (Rose Cottage)
Primitive Methodist Chapel
1  Kirby Samuel
2  Greeves Harry
3  Parker Herbert E
4  Curston Charles Frederick
5  Roper Thomas
6  Birdseye Alfred
7  Frost Sydney
8  Begley Arthur James  (grocer)
9  Parker JR
10 Collerson Miss

12  Watling Mrs
13  Ballard Cyril
14  Skippon Albert Herbert
14  Craske Arthur   (baker)
15  Hare Harry F
16  Futter Robert Richard
17  Fretwell Benjamin William
18  Sellers James

### Front Row Yard

Barnard Bertie James
Jones Thomas

———

19  Cott Mrs
**Reindeer PH   (Ernest Victor Fisher)**
*here are Stagg Row & Exhibition Terrace*

### East side

31  Toll Herbert
32  Lawler John Thomas
33  Crowther Albert Victor
34  Stimpson Mrs
35  Edwards Mrs
36  Franklin Mrs
37  Breeze Mrs
38  Turlink Mrs
39  Clarke Reginald. William
40  Fayres Alfred William
41  Stanforth William
42  Nicholls John
43  Fountain Walter
44  Lemon Sydney
*here are Garden Row & Double Row*
45  George Mrs
46  Skippon Herbert Albert
47  Sheldrake Frederick
48  Winter Frederick Mafeking
Hemeter John Ltd. (casings  manufacturer)
Hemeter Charles (Highgate House)
Bow Brand British Ltd. (tennis gut string manufacturers)

### FRONT ROW YARD

*See Front Row, Highgate*

Garden Row 1935. Silver Jubilee of King George V.

**FROST'S BUILDINGS**

*See Blackfriars Road*

**GARDEN ROW**

*From 26 Windsor Road*

East side

2  Seapy Alexander George
3  Rose Albert Edward

*here is Windsor Row*

West side

4  Broughton Miss
5  Catton Elijah

**GARDEN ROW (Highgate)**

*From 44 Front Row*

North side

1  High Arthur George
2  Mitchell Samuel William

3  Collison Joseph
4  Madder Mrs
5  Tinker William
6  Catling T
7  Addison Mrs
8  Shirley George
9  Bentley Percy
10  Kirby Robert
11  Gates Christopher
12  Neale Mrs
13  Fisher Ernest Victor
14  Dawson Walter
15  Turner Abraham
16  Benefer Henry
17  Wadlow Charles
18  Claxton James William

South side

19  Giles William H

## GARDEN ROW (Highgate) (continued)

20 Barber Robert
21 Booty Isaac
22 Massen Arthur
23 Gent James Henry
24 Hook Francis James
25 Buckle Joseph
26 —
27 —
28 Beakley Alfred
29 Curson Robert
30 Senter William
31 Rudd William
32 Ford William
33 Thorn Robert William
34 Langford Alfred
35 Fitt James

## GAYTON ROAD♦

*From 70 Lynn Road*
### South side
Rudd Herbert A
**The Swan PH (Walter Balls)**
Boulton Robert John (The Orchard)
Piper Cyril HV (decorator) (Senville)
Mann Alfred. James (Jeanville)
### Church cottages
Seals Mrs
Lane Thomas
Middleton Miss
Fysh Walter
Bates William

———

Drew Mrs E
Radcliffe Ven. Harry Sydney MA
(archdeacon of Lynn & rector)
(St. Faith's Rectory)
King's Lynn Clinic Ltd. (nursing home)
(Gaywood Hall)
### Cottage Row
1 Barrett John
2 Pointer Hy

3 Griffin Herbert
4 Riches Walter
5 Folkard William
6 Trundle William
7 Ellis William J
9 Gilding Elijah
10 Gilding Leonard

———

Hall Frederick (Fairstead Farm)
Bradshaw Dennis Stanley (Roseville)
Murdin Edward (Valrosa)
Cumberworth Rd. (Old Mill House)
### North side
Tebble John Percy (1 Chapel Cottages)
Housewes Elijah (2 Chapel Cottages)
Gaywood Conservative Club
(E Marshall (hon sec)
Blomfield Mrs M (corsetière) (Eden)
Dyke Frederick (Okay)
Binfield Misses (Grassendale)
Stibbon Arthur (relieving & vaccination
officer & collector & registrar of
births & deaths for Gayton sub-district)
Fitridge Frederick (Clandeboye)
Whittley Bernard Robert (Dunord)
Barker Herbert Whitmore (Carholme)
Allcock Herbert (Carr-Wood)
Warnes Geo. (Highbury)
*here is Field Road*
Wilkinson Rev. Michael MA
(assistant curate Gaywood parish church)
(The Old Field House)
Lane Geo. Stephens (School House)
Landles Edmnd. French (Gleniffer)
Smith Percy C (Fortismere)
Thomas Tudor G (Tolma)
Ramm AJL (Sledmere)
Diggle Thomas (Worthams)
Jermyn Oliver Reynolds (Silfield House)
Miles Sidney (Belstead lodge)
Barrett James M (Vallette)
Bloomfield Edward William (Woodhayes)

Gudgon Sydney (Red Thorns)
Godfrey Thomas Patchett (St.Stephen's)
Findlay Douglas H (Southbourne)
Crisp Alfred. Henry (Springwood)
Hopkins Harry (Intwood)
Bassett Martin Augustus  LDSRCS
(dental surgeon) (The Brown House)
Broughton James Albert (Thoresby)
Askew Ernest Graham (Sandiway)

**GAYWOOD ROAD**
*From Littleport Street to*
*Hunstanton railway crossing*
North side
*here is Front Row Highgate*
2a Capps Miss S  (confectioner)
2 Mann Richard  (fried fish shop)
4 Wiles Mrs S

6 Cock Ernest
8 Bush Robert
10 Dye Arthur H  (window cleaner)
12 Terry John
14 Rayner William
16 Brighton Charles Albert G
18 Keen Walter  Newlyn
20 Knape Edward & Son  (builders)
Dodman  Alfred & Co Ltd. (boiler makers)
24 Hammond John William
26 Bossingham John Edward
28 Houke George
30 Booth William
32 Parkes Anthony
34 Bowers Arthur Stanley
36 Holman Horace Lacey
38 Braybrook Harry
King's Lynn & District Working
Men's Co-operative Society Ltd.
(coal depot)
40 Martin Miss E
42 Watling Mrs
64 Taylor Robert  JP  (The Orchard)
66 Hilton Mrs EP  (Rose Villa)
68 —
70 —
72 Pichon Samuel Gypson
74 —
76 Parker Ralph
78 Cridland Edward
80 Fenn Albert Victor
82 Ivy Edgar
84 Spencer MM Victor
88 Watts Mrs
90 Nurse Miss
92 Langley Miss
94 Johnson William
96 Buck Robert William  (locksmith)
98 Tuffs Miss
100 Richards James Christopher
102 Whittome Frederick Edward
104 —

## GAYWOOD ROAD (continued)

106 Matthews Harry
108 Street George
110 Owen George E
112 & 114 **Woolpack PH  (Harry Fendley)**
*here is Tennyson Avenue*
116 Hopkins Harry
118 Williams Robert
120 McKenzie Claude
122 Hole Mrs
*here is King George the Fifth Avenue*
124 Cross Miss
126 Seamer S
128 Hignell William
130 Winter Harry
Gaywood Hospital
King Edward VII Grammar School
(Charles J L Wagstaff MA  headmaster)
*here is Hunstanton railway crossing*
*& King's Lynn boundary*

### South side

*here is Kettlewell Lane*
1 Reeve Edward
3 Foster JFB
5 Watson Herbert
7 Shaftoe Lewis
9 Howard Ernest
11 Coomber Miss Ethel
13 Temperton Mrs
15 Patfield Mrs
17 Mallett Mrs
*here is Eastgate Street*
19 **Spread Eagle PH    (John G Thomas)**
*here is lane leading to Archdale Street*
*here is Homeland Road*
21 Hares Frederick E
23 Linley Thomas Evelyn
25 Renaut Arthur Charles
27 Carlile Thomas William
29 Green Albert William  (dairyman)
*here is Salter's Road*
Swan Laundry Ltd.

Highgate Council Infants' School
31 Scott William
33 Rose Miss (Congregational)
35 Kemp Miss
37 Bradfield Miss
39 Affleck Mrs
41 Burlingham Miss Priscilla Mary
43 Langley Thomas FW  (deputy superintendent registrar for Freebridge Lynn district)
45 Davey Clifford
47 Eagleton Mrs
49 Sharpe Frederick
51 Williams Mrs
53 Campbell Thomas
55 Regester Miss G
57 Mussett James Edward
59 Freeman Herbert
61 Bower Rev. CR   (Primitive Methodist)
63 Back Miss F
65 Duff Misses
67 Goodley Mrs
69 Donaldson Mrs
71 Larwood George James
73 Chilvers Robert Henry
75 Hitchcock Roger Castell
77 Brett Mrs AM
79 Bush Francis Albert
81 Taylor Mrs
83 Rasberry Walter
85 Carnell JL
87 Vickers David
89 Eagleton Ernest
91 Holmes Captain Albert E
93 Wilkinson Joseph W  (insurance superintendent)
95 Hamson Joseph
97 Liverpool Victoria Friendly Society (H Nicholson, district manager)
99 Miles Albert
101 Jones William
103 Matthew John C

A van leaves Gaywood Road to cross over the Hunstanton railway line (the border of Lynn and Gaywood village) to Lynn Road. This picture was used to show the 'bottle-neck' caused by the encroachment of gates into the road.
Apparently pedestrians preferred to use the road rather than the special gates provided!

## GAYWOOD ROAD (continued)

105 Hunter Benjamin D'Arcy
107 Hardy Mrs
109 Hardy Miss
111 Catton Valentine Charles
113 Wolfe William
115 Neale James
117 Goss Miss
119 Dow Horace
121 Cockle William H
123 Sooby Miss
125 Pilling John
127 Youngs John H
129 Whitehead samuel
131 Birtwistle WDB
133 Wheeler Leslie Charles
135 Langley Benjamin William
137 Skinner Lewis
139 Page Dudley S
141 Bell Mrs
143 Webb Charles
145 Bolton Robert
147 Best Samuel

149 Palmer Alfred
151 Twaits Ernest
153 Twaits Miss
155 Hall Mrs
157 Dickerson Samuel
159 Martin James H
161 —

## GEORGE STREET

*From Hextable Road to 58 Loke Road*

### West side

2 Bone George
3 Sharpin Mrs
4 Howard William
5 —
6 Worfolk Gerald
8 Farr Mrs
9 Barnaby George
10 Brock George
11 Brittain James Henry
12 Yallop Arthur (teacher of pianoforte)
13 Yallop Mrs
14 Howard Mrs

## GEORGE STREET (continued)

15  Frost Mrs
16  Futter Harry
17  Fiddiment Albert
18  Richardson William
19  Gent Mrs
20  Howard James
21  Hastings Mrs
22  Bone James W
23  Crome Robert
24  Stallard Jack
25  Westfield Charles
26  Goodson William, Carter
26  Goodson Walter EW  (radio engineer)
27  Arnell Mrs

### East side

29  Barker Mrs
30  Burton Mrs
31  Pells George Ernest
32  Case Victor Frederick
33  Pells Mrs
34  Pells Thomas James
35  Richardson Frederick
36  Richards Harry J
37  Anderson Mrs
38  Sheppson J
39  Earl William
40  Skerritt Frederick G
41  Ransom Mrs
42  Tann William
43  Leverett Thomas
44  Sheppardson Albert Robert Thomas
45  Jarvis Mrs
46  Earl Mrs
47  Regester William
48  Farr Thomas
49  Ess James
50  Regester Samuel
51  Malt James
52  Jerry Mrs
53  Harper Mrs
54  Gore Josiah

55  Regester Robert Henry
56  Fuller George
57  Ransome Mrs Frances  (shopkeeper)

## GEORGE YARD
### From 23 Norfolk Street

1  Juby Mrs
2  Shallow Robert
3  Gill William
4  Skipper Miss
Couperthwaite WM & Sons (ironmongers - workshop)
5  Sellers Frederick
6  Goldsmith Alex
7  —
8  Smith Mrs F
9  Roper William

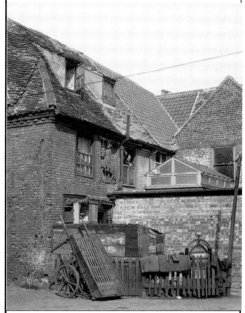

George Yard . The recently extended property is the rear of 23/24 Norfolk Street - owned by FG Kirkland (tailor). Note the sculpture of Saint George in the wall.

## GILBERT ROW
*From 45 London Road*

1 Arch Ronald
2 Frost Francis John
3 Bennison Frederick
4 Page Mrs
5 Hooks John Edward
6 Hardy John Thomas
7 Wilson Leslie

## GLADSTONE ROAD
*From 2 Friars Street to The Friars*
### South side

1 Sheldrick John
2 Bennett Thomas
3 Joplin Leonard
4 Jex Edward Ernest
5 Melton Gordon
6 Mansfield William
7 Foster James Dobson
8 Groom Joseph
9 Peacock Eric
10 Trundle Sydney
11 Lincoln Miss ME
12 Palfrey Miss Isobel
13 Naylor Walter
14 Kidd Ernest William
14 Kidd Leslie William G (insurance agent)
15 Triscott Mrs
16 Smith Thomas
17 Trundle George Frederick
18 Spooner Benjamin
19 Reed George
20 Bracey Edward James
21 Walker Frederick  (butcher)
22 Bracebridge Mrs

## GOODWIN VILLAS
*See Goodwin's Road*

## GOODWIN'S ROAD
*From Windsor Road to Exton's Road*
### West side

1 Barrett Mrs
2 Mclntosh John Morrison
Bridges Mrs (Beech House)
Pank Alfred William (Laurel House)
Munford Frank Ernest (Hillington Cottage)
### North side
Heath Alfred  (Holly Lodge)
Norman Miss AM (Brookfield)
Bartle Mrs Alice (Glenthorne)
Hancock Harold N (Lyndhurst)
Hovell John (Sunnymayes)
Teasel William W (Benderlock)
*here is Guanock Terrace*
### South-east side
Martin James H.  FBHS  (nurseryman)
(Chase nurseries)
Sucker John (Northcote)
Davy John (Sherwood House)
Whitmore John (Heathcote)
Chatterton Percival T   JP (Thurlow House)
Jackson Donald F. (Hamilton House)
Watkins Eric Holmes BA, BM, BCh
(physician & surgeon)  (Eskdale)
Wandford Mrs (Rosedale)
Leake Charles Robert (Plaxtole)
Johnson Mrs William (Woodleigh)
Thomas Mrs (Brooklyn Villa)
### East side
Clarke Major Herbert (Norfolk House)
Howard Henry Miles (Fern villa)
Crawford Rev. Alexander Johnstone MA (Oxon)
(rector of South Lynn All Saints) (The Rectory)
Parsons James A  BA (Sunnyside)
Convent of Our Lady of Walsingham
(High Class Secondary Day School)
Woodwark Col. George Graham CBE, TD, JP
(Croyland)
Smithard Edmund G  JP (Glenville)
Lemmon Charles Herbert (Redcroft)

Goodwin's Road looking towards Guanock Terrace

## GOODWIN'S ROAD (continued)

Adams Herbert Hilditch (Mountfield)
Potter Miss EH   (Springfield)
Springall Oliver Steel (Runcton House)
Cockle Ernest (Arncliffe Cottage)

### North side
### Goodwin villas

1  Slator Mrs
2  Murrell James Nelson

———

Hammond Oswald S (Sidney House)
Heseltine Wilfrid (Silverdale House)
Bradshaw AC & Co (potato agents) (Silverdale House)

### Backham's almshouses

1  Jude Mrs
2  Copeman Mrs
3  Crow Mrs
4  Attwood Mrs
5 —

———

Anderson George Howard (Fairlight Lodge)
Le Grice Charles C  (Elmer lodge)

### Sugar's almshouses

6  Hopkins Mrs

5  Sharman Mrs
4  Barker Mrs
3  Bannister Mrs
2  Parsons Mrs
1  Futter Mrs

## GRAHAM STREET
*From 22 Exton's Road*
### East side

1  Collier John Henry
2  Coupland Alfred Ernest
3  Salt Cyril Henry
4  Rasberry George David
5  Williamson Mrs
6  Petchey Mrs
7  Skippon Mrs H
8  Whalls Mrs E
9  Sexton Miss E
10  Greenacre Robert Ernest

### West side
*here is Russell Street*

11  Austrin Philip Thomas
12  Lake Walter
13  Booty Alfred. Valentine
14  Howling Frank
15  Hudson Robert Osbourne

## GREYFRIARS ROAD

*From Stonegate Street to London Road*

### North side

*here is Tower Place*

1 —
2 Summers Ernest Martin
St. Margaret's (C of E) Schools
(boys, girls & infants)
Mitchell Miss E (Infants' School House)
Dodman James (School House)

## GRUMMETS YARD

*From 9 Providence Street*

Reeve Albert Edward

## GUANOCK PLACE

*continuation of Guanock Terrace*
*to London Road*

1 Chilvers John
2 Chilvers Mrs
3 Knight Harry
4 Scott Mrs Sarah
5 Blackburn James
6 Cruickshank Kenneth
7 Coates Daniel John (corn merchant)
8 —
9 —
10 Peacock Herbert
11 Castle Richard

## GUANOCK TERRACE

*From Goodwin's Road to Guanock Place*

### East side

1 **Lord Napier Inn (Joseph Sanderson Hall)**
3 Curtis Mrs
5 Laws Mrs
7 Rutherford James Henry
*here is Thomas Street*
9 Dennis Frederick William (grocer)
11 Haylett Albert
13 Dennis Frederick James
15 Overton Robert

17 Newham Brothers (shoeing smiths)
19 Fox Mrs
21 Hovell Thomas William
23 Reed Frederick
25 Newham Mrs
27 Kerrison Wilfrid
29 Mindham John Thomas
31 Booty Alfred. Paul
33 Gant Frederick
35 Harrod Ralph E
37 Hart Frank
39 Deans Arthur
41 Kirby Henry
43 Edwards John Thomas Newton (baker)
*here is Charles Street*

### West side

2 Dye Robert William
4 Whiley Alfred Henry
6 Frost Miss EA
8 Norfolk Dairies (Alcock & Appleby)
8 Crowe Mrs
10 Williams George
12 Hudson Walter. Edward
14 Mountser Miss
16 Aldridge Mrs
18 Mitchell Eric George
20 Hodd Mrs JS
22 Green Frederick
24 Green William George
26 Newstead Mrs MA
Renaut Brothers (builders) (workshop)
28 Jubey Charles (bricklayer)
30 Whincop Mrs
32 Drew Robert Jonathan
34 Bland William
36 Catton Mrs
38 Ebbens Alfred Victor
40 Ebbens John
44 Scott Arthur (wholesale grocer)
46 Barker Victor A (pianoforte tuner)
48a Plowright Frederick Henry (boot repairer)
48 Vice Albert Edward

## GUANOCK TERRACE (continued)

49  Mayes George
Hill Thomas Benjamin  (wireless dealer)

### HALF MOON YARD*
*From 29 Pilot Street*

1  Hudson Herbert Ernest
2  Hardy George Henry

### HAMPTON COURT
*From 3 Nelson Street*

1  Sinnott Miss M F
2  Pottle George Edward
3  Armes Miss
4  Depear William Henry
5  Gaze Percy Frank
6  Hitchcock Frederick Joseph J
6  Giles Edward R  (electrical engineer)

7  Fuller William Robert
8  Langton Mrs S
9  Jones Miss Rose

### HANOVER YARD
*See St. Ann's Street*

### HANWELL'S YARD*
*From 22 Pilot Street*

2  Griffin John Stanley
4  Day John William

### HARDWICK NARROWS
*From Hardwick Road*

Garrod William
Crook William
Ellyard Robert
Beach Frederick

ESSENTIAL TO TOWN'S FUTURE PROSPERITY

Plea to Avoid Site Near Residential Areas

HOW PYLONS SPOILT SUITABLE PLACE

MAYOR OUTLINES PLAN FOR A LYNN AIRPORT

This pylon carrying 133,000 volts off Hardwick Road proved to be a stumbling block to a plan for Lynn's municipal airport in 1934.

## HARDWICK ROAD
*From South Gates*

Skerry Mrs (Locum)
Barber Mrs (Ivydene)
Oakes AE (Red May)
Neal George Lawrence (The Riviera)
Jeckells Herbert George (Delhi)
Wheeler Leslie Charles (Croyde)
Smith John William (The Haven)
Figg Frank (Deganwy)
Cook Charles (Cambrai)
Mowton Walter (Ashburton)
*here is Beech Road*
King's Lynn Borough Cemetery
(Mrs Charlotte Eliza Melton (curator)
Edwards Samuel (Hardwick Bridge
bungalow)

### Railway cottages
1  Pearce PH
2  Witting Stanley C
3  Rust Mrs
4  Britton Alfred
5  Barrett Mrs
6  Norman George

## HARROD'S YARD
*From 3 Providence Street*

6  Brown Alfred
7  Brown Miss Rose
8  Judd William
9  Woodhouse Ernest
10  Newson George Edward
11  Green Edward Charles
12  Harris Albert
13  Bishop William

## HART'S YARD*
*From 5 Pilot Street*

1  Foster William L
2  Fuller Cyril Stanley
3  Burch Wilfred
4  Fisher Frank

Hart's Yard, Pilot Street in 1933.

## HAYLETT TERRACE
*See Exton's Road*

## HEXTABLE ROAD
*From Pilot Street*

Balls Albert Edward (shell fish merchant)
Bone & Sons  (shell fish merchants)
*here are Lansdowne, Birchwood*
*& George Streets*

## HIGH ROAD
*See Saddlebow*

6 & 7 Hartley GM Ltd (ladies' & children's outfitters & general drapers)

*here is Law's Yard*

8 **Cheshire Cheese PH** (Frederick Claude John Carpenter)

9 Millers (late Pamment & Smith) (music & gramophone dealers)

*here is Armes Yard*

10, 11, 12, 13, 14, 15 & 16 Jermyn & Sons Ltd (drapers & furnishers)

*here is Union Lane*

17 Count Sydney (photographic & dispensing chemist)

17 Smith James & Son Ltd. (dyers)

17a Pumfreys (costumier)

18 Turner W & E Ltd. (boot makers)

19 Murdoch & Murdoch & Co. (Pianoforte Manufacturers)

*here is Kendrick's Yard*

20 Lennards Ltd. (boot makers)

21 & 22 Le Grice Brothers (drapers)

23 Smith WH & Son Ltd (newsagents)

23a Biggs H Hindley

## HIGH STREET

*From Saturday Market Place to Tuesday Market Place*

### East side

#### Smith's Chambers

Kleen-e-ze-Brush Co. Ltd

Prudential Assurance Co Ltd (HW Spinks, district superintendent)

1 Eastern Counties Omnibus Co Ltd

1 Smith Brothers (tobacconists)

2 Crook Joseph & Son Ltd (hosiers)

3 Pullars of Perth (dyers)

3a Hamblin Theodore Ltd. (opticians)

4 Barrett CG & Co (steam laundry)

4a Lown & Capps (printers)

5 Cranfield Alex (jeweller)

5a Colby Arthur John

24 & 25 Collins' Agency (servants' registry office)

24 & 25 Hepworth J & Son Ltd. (clothiers)

*here is Sedgeford Lane*

26 Hiltons Ltd. (boot makers)

*here is New Conduit Street*

34 Street George Ernest (outfitter)

35 London Central Meat Co. Ltd. (butchers)

36 Foster Bros. Clothing Co Ltd (outfitters)

37 Star Supply Stores (grocers)

38 Walton Brothers (tailors)

39 Maypole Dairy Co. Ltd

39, 40 & 41 Ladyman JH & Co. Ltd (wholesale & retail grocers)

42 Hipps Ltd. (clothiers)

43 & 44 Boots Cash Chemists (Eastern) Ltd

45 **Queen's Head PH (Walter E Williamson)** - (from October 1933)

46 Street SG (pianoforte warehouse)

47 Freeman Hardy & Willis Ltd (boot makers)

48 & 49 Goddard George (outfitter)

50 Winlove-Smith Charles Ltd (confectioners)

51 Bradfields (drapers & ladies' outfitters)

52 Clough Thomas & Son (gun makers & sports dealers)

53a Johnson Bros. (dyers) Ltd

53 Hudson Herbert (tobacconist)

54 Empson Jonathan H (jeweller)

55 Allen & Neale (Chemists) Ltd

*here is Norfolk Street*

56a Emmerson & Youngman (ladies' hairdressers)

It's 8.30pm on a winter's evening at the junction of High Street and Norfolk Street and there is not a soul about. The pubs will close at 10.30pm.

A bright sunny Tuesday morning in High Street in the Spring of 1937. At the junction of High Street and Norfolk Street is probably the most popular shop in town, 'FW Woolworth Co Ltd $3^d$ and $6^d$ Store' (right of picture) - the forerunner of today's pound shops.

56  Briggs & Co.  (boot makers)
57 & 58 Marks & Spencer Ltd.  (bazaar)
60 —
61 Hiltons Ltd  (boot makers)
62 Williams Miss Marjorie  (gowns)

**Midland Chambers**

63 & 64 Mapus-Smith & Lemmon (accountants)
63 & 64 Midland Bank Ltd. (Frank Coooper, manager)
63 & 64 Pearl Assurance Co. Ltd.

——

West side

65  Jones & Dunn  (gents' outfitters)
66  Ann & Co.  (antique brass reproductions & fancy goods)

67  Le Roi  (dyers)
68  Halford Cycle Co. Ltd. (cycle makers)
69  Targett  PS  (stationer)
70  Adlam WJ  MPS, FSMC (chemist & optician)
71  Peatling Thomas & Sons Ltd.  (wine & spirit merchants)
72  Kirk Robert  (boot maker)
73 & 74 Woolworth FW & Co. Ltd. (bazaar)
75  Couperthwaite WM & Sons (ironmongers)
76  Easiephit Shoe Co Ltd
77  Midlands  (florist)
78  Cox & Son  (cycle dealers)
79 Eastern Evening News
79 Eastern Daily Press (Norfolk News Co Ltd)
79 Eastern  Weekly Press

TOP: Belfast Linen Warehouse (linen drapers) at 89 High Street in 1935.
ABOVE: High Street in 1935. Celebrating in style for King George V Silver Jubilee.

Looking down High Street from the Saturday Market Place on a bright late morning in c1936. The sign indicating Jermyn's is visible further down the street.
A street light casts its shadow over the cobbled street.

## HIGH STREET (continued)

80 King William J   (jeweller)
81 Burlingham SS Ltd.   (jewellers)
81b Church of England Young Men's Society
82 Curry's Cycle Co.   (cycle dealers)
83 Metcalf Charles Francis   (plumber)
84 Goodchild PM   (photographer)

### Purdy's Court

84a Harper Smiths, Hayhow & Co. (incorporated accountants)
84a Dance Studio (Mrs WH Rutter & Miss W Winlove-Smith)

————

85 Rose John & Son   (fancy leather dealers)
86 Emmerson & Youngman (ladies' hairdressers)
87 Cash & Co.   (boot makers)
88 Belfast Linen Warehouse (linen drapers)
89 Speed & Son   (watch makers, jewellers & silversmiths)
90 Fleming, Reid & Co. Ltd. (scotch wool stores)
91 to 97 Scott & Son (house furnishers)

*here is Purfleet Street*

The Corner House Tea Rooms
98 Smith PC   (watch maker)
98 Barrett Mrs E   (confectioner)
99 Fletcher W & R Ltd.   (butchers)
100 Greig David Ltd. (provision dealers)
101 Crosskill Miss Ida   (confectioner)
102 Fell S & Sons Ltd.   (cycle dealers)
103 International Tea Co.'s Stores Ltd (grocers)
103a Hole Mrs Jane   (children's outfitter)
103b Hunters Ltd.   (grocers)

*here is Baker Lane*

104 Davis Harry   (fruiterer)
105 & 106 Hamson Joseph   (pawnbroker)
107 Home & Colonial Stores Ltd.   (grocers)
108 —
109 —
110 —

111 Lipton Ltd   (provision merchants)
112 Adcock & Son   (tobacconists)
113 Salter & Salter (1900) Ltd.   (boot makers)
114 Bennell FW & Son   (bakers)
114a Wigram & Ware Ltd.   (opticians)
114b Jermyn & Sons Ltd.   (staff residence)
115,116 & 117 Letzer Ethel   (milliner)
118 —
119 Pugh & Son   (hosiers)
120 Barnards   (fruiterers)
120 (back of)  Hall & Stringer   (cabinet makers)
120a Neal & Son   (plumbers)
121 & 122 Andrews Thomas William (butcher)
123 **Wenn's Hotel   (Preston M Rush)**

### HILDON'S YARD*
*From 108 Norfolk Street*

1 Reed Walter. Matthew
2 Cheetham Frederick
3 Howe Isaac
4 Bailey Miss
5 Newdick Albert  senior
6 Kent Robert
7 Newdick Albert  junior
8 McCowen John Joseph
9 Hewerson Horace
10 Brown Francis  William
11 Hunt Frederick Joseph
12 Sellers Miss
13 Bracher Frederick Charles
14 Mann Samuel Henry

### HILLINGTON SQUARE
*From 28 Providence Street*

Swallow Clement H   (shopkeeper)
Tyzack  Charles Z
Woods Alfred. B
1 Bailey George Samuel
2 Gotsell Alfred
3 Sherriff Mrs Emma

Hildon's Yard, off Norfolk Street, in 1933

**HILLINGTON SQUARE (continued)**

4 Goldsmith Percy
5 Gaunt Kelhan
6 Emerson Wilfrid Redvers
7 Carr Gordon Lloyd
8 Hill Henry Richard
9 Hewett Reginald
10 —
11 Betts Miss
12 Woods John
13 Pearman Alfred. Samuel
14 Fitridge Frederick
15 Edgley Edgar
16 —
17 Bocking George
18 Edlinton Mrs SA
19 Harper Arthur
20 Henry Bert Thomas
22 Morgan Harry Douglas
23 Branham George Henry
24 Howells David B
25 Plowright Richard

26 Wright Stanley
27 Cross James Henry
28 Pilgrim Mrs SA
29 Eagle George

## HOCKHAM STREET
*From Diamond Terrace*
*to Hockham Terrace*
East side

1 Beaty Mrs Ellen E (grocer)
3 Harvey Charles
5 Terrey George Win
7 Gittens Frederick
9 Beales Thomas Frederick
11 Williamson John Robert
13 Alexander Clifford
15 Kirby James Francis
17 Hammond Mrs
19 Gibson Herbert Charles
21 Harrod Alfred
23 Smith Frederick Dobson
25 Smith Hubbard Francis
27 Raven Mrs
29 Richardson Charles William
31 Raines Alfred
33 Rout Daniel
35 Peck Edwin
37 Bass Harry

West side

8 Plowright Mrs EA
10 Tuck Robert
12 Richardson John
14 Hickman Frederick
16 Proctor Fred
18 Chapman Samuel
20 Tuck Walter Edmund
22 Guy Ernest John
24 Gurney Robert
26 Spaxman David PN
28 Chapman Frederick
30 Reed Mrs M
32 Smith Henry

## HOCKHAM STREET (continued)

34 Baxter William
36 Hand Walter Herbert
38 Hewitt Charles
40 Goodman Gerald
42 Weldrick Henry John Thomas
44 Harper William George

## HOCKHAM TERRACE

*From 14 Lancaster Terrace*

1 Defty James Edmund
2 Brandon Charles
3 Hand Herbert
4 Neeve William
5 Green Henry James
6 Wanford Albert Edward
7 Fisher William
8 Simpson Mrs
9 Williamson George William
10 Starling Frederick James
11 Peake George Davey
12 Carter Thomas Albert
18 Violen William John

## HOLCOMBE AVENUE

*From Exton's Road*
### West side

1 Dunwoody Mrs MM
2 Jennings Charles Leslie
3 Ransom Edward
4 Neilson James
5 Robinson Mrs
6 Spreckley Harold Charles
7 Brook Leslie
8 Baldock Frank
9 Davison John Ernest
10 Raby John William  JP
### East side
11 Gilbert Reginald. James
12 Cairns Arthur John
13 Tann Herbert
14 Creasey Arthur Mortimer

15 Franklin Arthur
16 Brinn Albert Edgar
17 Greenfield William Henry
18 Dunbabin Charles Thomas

## HOMELAND ROAD

*From 21 Gaywood Road*
### North side

1 Goodson Miss
2 Foster Joseph Parkin
3 Ives Robert
4 Blyth John William
5 Langstaff Archibald
6 Hazell Leslie
7 Triance Mrs S
### South side
8 Moate George
9 Hall Harold
10 Dersley William (insurance superintendent)
11 Teucher Herman
12 Fortnam Walter Henry
Butcher George  (Dereham House)

## HORSELEY'S CHASE

*From Hardwick Road*
Port Isolation Hospital (JR Gibson, caretaker)

## HORSLEYS COURT

*From 7 Southgate Street*

1 Bowen Mrs
2 Chapman Mathew
3 Ashton Miss EJ
4 Gibson Mrs S

## HOSPITAL WALK

*From London Road to 17 Windsor Terrace*
### Wellington Cottages

4 Medlock Mrs
3 Pitt Mrs
2 Guyton Ernest
1 Riches Robert Henry
*here are Keppel & Victoria Streets*

## HOSPITAL WALK (continued)

1 Gordon Alfred. Charles
2 Godbolt Ernest
3 Rees William Ernest
4 Collison Alfred
5 Bone George Frank
6 Pettit William Frederick

## JOHN STREET

*From 24 South Everard Street to*
*20 North Everard Steet*
### North-west side

1 Renaut Arthur William
2 Bullen Charles Robert
3 Brittain Frank
4 Hendry Mrs
5 Barnes Walter George
   *here are St. John's Cottages*
6 Watson Harry B
7 Ebbens Herbert George
8 Howlett Frederick
9 Hall Arthur Percy

### South-east side

10  Bogg Arthur A

## JOHNSON'S SQUARE
*See Albert Street*

## JUBILEE TERRACE
*See Saddlebow Road*

## KEMBLE'S YARD
*From 75 Friars Street*

2 Culpritt Benjamin
3 Francis Herbert
4 Smith Bertie
5 Robinson William Arthur

Kemble's Yard in 1933. This was issued with a clearance order in 1936.

## KEPPEL STREET

*From 5 Windsor Road to Hospital Walk*

### West side

1  Jackson Arthur William
2  Morris Mrs F
3  Holden Alfred Victor
4  Palmer Mrs
5  Watson William Robert
6  Thoday Mrs
7  Dix Charles
8  Toll Victor
9  Eagle Hector Baden
10  Fysh Mrs FN
11  Brown Robert
12  Horsley Miss
13a  Bird Frederick
14a  Crane Mrs R
15a  Moores Harold
16a  Taylor Bertie
17a  Eke Mrs EG
18a  Watson Henry John
19a  Massingham Earl
20a  Holland Harry Edmund

### East side

21  Bushell Mrs EA
22  Banner Mrs
23  Brown John Robert
24  Lyon Horace
25  Wagg Henry
26  Jackson Mrs
27  Hardy William Percy
28  Gray Mrs
14  Ewen Mrs MA
15  Mitchell Edward William David
16  Anderson James Valentine
17  Dixon Frederick George Self
18  Baldwin Bertie
19  Chilvers John Henry
20  Tucker Stuart A

## KETTLE WELL LANE

*From Littleport Street*

1  Rennie Mrs
2  Leveritt Mrs
3  Andrews Horace Ambrose
4  Willings Mrs
5  Foreman Brittiff Laws  (builder)
Jackson Charles W (Kettlewell House)
Corporation Electricity Works & Offices
(Charles William Jackson MIEE (chief engineer)

## KING STREET

*From Purfleet Place to
Tuesday Market Place*

### West side

*here is Purfleet Quay*

1 —
3 Tracy Nathaniel   LDSRFPS (dental surgeon)
3 Chadwick Morley BA, MRCS Eng, LRCP Lond. (surgeon medical officer) (& public vaccinator & police surgeon)
5 Coxon Major Stephen Arthur Thomas TD, JP, LDSRCSI (dental surgeon)
5 Coxon Capt. Arthur Cedric Mears MA, MB, BCh. Cantab, MRCS, LRCP Lond., LDSRCS (dental surgeon)
Bullen Mrs  (Ouse House)
9 Blunt Thornton
11 Inland Revenue Office (tax department)
11 Trenowath & Son (furniture removers)
11 Hutton Potts Mrs AC
11 Sutton & Co. Ltd.  (general carriers)
13 Mosse BE Tenison BA Cantab, MRCS, LRCP  (physician & surgeon)
15 Ayre Miss
17 Dean David M  MB, BSLond, MRCS LRCP   (physician & surgeon)

### Langley's Yard (Aickman's Yard)

Langley & Son  (gate manufacturers)

## KING STREET (continued)

Greeves Mrs
Errington Mrs

_____

19 Hayes George Arthur (clerk to the
Freebridge Lynn Rural District Council
& superintendent registrar)
19 Langley Thomas FW (deputy supt.
Registrar Lynn district)
19 Fitridge FW (assistant clerk to the
Freebridge Lynn Rural District Council &
acting registrar of marriages)
21 West Norfolk & King's Lynn
High School for Girls (Miss R Williamson BA,
headmistress)
21 Williamson Miss R
*here is Ferry Lane*
23 Ancient Order of Foresters (F G Hitchcock,
secretary)
23 Blyth William Henry Parker
25 Hyner William John  (solicitor)
25 Reed, Wayman & Hyner  (solicitors)
25a Jackson Charles Headley
27 Bridges GM & Son Ltd. (scenic
bazaars)
29 Bridges AB  (Shakespeare House)
**Globe Hotel  (Frederick George W Hayes)**
### East side
*here is Purfleet Street*
2 —
4 Shears Arthur
6 Coulton & Son  (solicitors)
6 Bush Francis Alfred (clerk to the NCC Guardians Committee) (& superintendent registrar)
6  Quisee Edwin Thomas (collector to the NCC
Guardians Committee & registrar of marriages)
8 Ream Miss
10 Steward & Patteson Ltd.  (brewers)
12 Bradfer-Lawrence H L (H. Marsh) land agent
14 Britton Mrs
14a Bunkle Miss ME  (tailoress)
16 —

*here is Thompson's Yard*
20 Jewson Miss
20 Jewson Alfred E (photographer)
22 Metcalf Bros.   (plumbers)
24 Barnes AB (incorporating Durrant &
Wright), (auctioneer [tithe] estate agent)
24 King's Lynn & West Norfolk Permanent
Benefit Building Society (RV Hyde, sec)
24 Hyde Reginald Vincent (assessor & collector
of taxes for King's Lynn)
26 Jones Henry JJ
28 Lincoln Maurice
30  Women's Conservative Club (Mrs W Catleugh, sec)
32 Barker Albert George  (clerk & sexton) St
Margaret's church
32 Barker John
34 Spinks John
36 Joyner James  (tailor)
38 Eagleton & Andrews  (architects)
38 Royal Insurance Co. Ltd. (GR
Alexander, resident inspector)
40 Dennis John H   (baker)
42 Whitrick William
44 Parsons James Ambrose BA Camb (solicitor
& commissioner for oaths)
44 Customs & Excise (H Gibbons, surveyor);
CM Suggett, officer of 1st station; BE Bremner,
officer of 2nd station)
46 Dennick John Herbert

## KING STREET (continued)
48 Clough LG
50 Benefer Peter
52 Sennett Frank Elliott   (sail maker)

## KING GEORGE THE FIFTH AVENUE
*From 122 Gaywood Road*
### West side
1 Ofley Miss C
2 Andrews Frederick S
3 Eaton Robert M
4 Lemmon Hubert
5 Hillam Horace
6 Stanford John Henry
7 Neave Spencer
8 Nuthall .Miss K
9 Gibbons Hubert
10 Freestone CA
11 Flowerday Edward George
Alderton Ronald Trevor (Denver House)

## KING STAITH LANE
*From 15 Queen Street*
Floyd William Henry  (poultry food
manufacturer) [King Staith Mill]

## KING STAITH SQUARE
1 Fayers Robert William & Sons (builders)
2 Humphreys Miss Dorothy
CSMMG, MLICh. (masseuse,
medical electric treatment & chiropodist)
2 Turner-Jones Miss Muriel G,
MISCh. Lond, MNAC  (chiropodist)
3 Hutton  Thomas Oswald MB, MCPS
(physician & surgeon & medical officer
3 Sexton John   MB, BCh, BAONUI
(physician & surgeon)
Coleman Walter  (Bank House)
Crundall Percy
Smith WR & Son (ship brokers)
Fison Packard & Prentice Ltd.
(fertiliser merchants)

## KING'S AVENUE
*From 7 Exton's Place*
1  Free Frederick
2  Wheeler Percy Frederick
3  Hill Henry Rd
4  Edge George
5  Hudson Walter. Harry
6  Copsey James
7  Catchpole Samuel Charles
8  Bowman John James
9  Barnard Mrs
10  Richmond Charles Herbert
11  Reeve William Gunton

## KIRBY STREET
*From 64 Norfolk Street to Wellesley Street*
### East side
1  Rutland Arthur RV
2  Adams Ernest  (boot repairer)
3  Brighton Mrs
4  Ballard William
5  Gore William Edward
6  Jude Frederick
6a Seymour Arthur T
7  Capps John
8  Fox Mrs
9  Warne Frank
10  Stebbings Albert William  (shopkeeper)
11  Hooke Albert Victor
12  Walker Spenton
13  Coleman Mrs
14  Walker Ernest Edward
15  Willis Walter
16  Marsters Leonard
17  Hobbs Harry
### West side
18  Langley James
19  Foreman Mrs SA
20  Baker George
21  Foreman Mrs E
*here is Broadway*
22  —

In 1934 this fine example of a Georgian building which backed on to the Purfleet in King Staith Square was owned by William Fayers & Sons (builders & undertakers). It was originally built as a dwelling house and was by now in a poor state of repair and only survived to 1935 when a new silo was built on the site.

## KIRBY STREET (continued)

23  Rayner Arthur
23a  —
24a  Tipple Mrs S
24  Winterton Mrs
25  Giles Mrs
26  Valentine George
27  Fox Edmund
28  Seaman James
29  Gunns Archibald
30  Neale George William
Gray JR  (garage)
32  Eagleton Samuel Thomas
33  Allen Mrs

## KITCHENER STREET

*From 85 Saddlebow Road*

### North side

*here is Atbara Terrace*

30 Giles William Ernest  (hardware dealer)
13 Elwin Frederick James
15 Uttin Samuel William
17 Slegg Alfred
17 Allen Miss Maud  (dressmaker)
19 Hardy John William
21 Taylor Thomas Edgar
23 Hewitt Walter Frederick
25 Brighton Charles Edward

### South side

14 Shinn James
16 Catton Mrs A
18 Foreman Arthur Frederick
20 Uttin James

## KITCHENER STREET (continued)

22 Wagge Charles Edgar
24 Rout William
26 Mortimer Harry
28 Crome William Leslie
31 Hodgson William Ernest
32 —

## LAKE'S YARD
*From 7 High Street*

## LANCASTER TERRACE
*From 7 Portland Place*
*to 25 Langham Street*

1 Mann Frederick Charles
2 Pitt John
3 King Cyril
4 Lift Arthur
5 Palmer Alfred
6 Williamson John
7 Smith William
8 Haverson Christopher
9 Ebling Jack
10 Raven Robert
11 Rope Sidney John (fried fish shop)

## LANGHAM STREET
*From Diamond Terrace*
### East side

1 Moriss William Charles
3 Juby Frederick Flun Lewis
5 Howell Edward
7 Brown Albert Charles
9 Allen William
11 Colby Walter
13 Polyn Walter
15 Dunning James Henry
17 Burke Mrs S
19 Ford John William
21 Whalebelly Walt George
23 Cullen George
25 Melton Robert William

### West side

2 Easton John William
4 Graves Charles Percy
6 Hart Richard
8 Beales Frederick
10 Cole George Henry
12 Moxon Francis
14 Fayers Reuben
16 Todd Elijah
15 Arrowsmith Thomas William
20 Gathercole George
22 Dickerson Mrs
24 Hall Mrs
26 Greenwood Palmer
32 Overman James
34 Fisher George Edward
36 Drew Charles Henry
38 Tidd William Thomas

## LANGLEY'S YARD
*See King Street*

## LANSDOWNE STREET
*From Hextable Road to 36 Loke Road*
### East side

1 Balls Mrs E
2 Hall Augustus
3 Smith John Thomas
4 Pratt Sidney
5 Nuccoll Arthur
6 Regester Mrs
7 Barker Frederick
8 Stevenson Alex
9 Neal Mrs
10 Mitchelson Albert
11 Carter John
12 Leman Arthur
13 Goodson Harry
14 Addison Frederick
15 Collison William
16 Bobbin Edward James
17 Horsley Edward

Law's Yard, High Street in 1933.

## LANSDOWNE STREET (continued)

18 Whiley John
19 Scrutton Charles
20 Pooley Arthur
21 Leman Reuben
22 Fisher Frederick

### West side

23 King's Lynn & District Working
Men's Co-operative Society Ltd
24 Pycroft Percy
25 Butcher walter Mark
26 Bushell Frederick Robert
27 Fysh Charles Arthur
28 Worfolk William L
29 Belton Robert John
30 Bennell George Andrew
31 Johnson James
32 Pryor Percy M
33 Flanders Joseph
34 Richardson Thomas
35 Ely Joseph
36 Jaggs Robert George

37 Earl Mrs Elizabeth   (shopkeeper)
38 Link Mrs
39 Panton Joseph
40 Anderson SJ
41 Bunn Edward B
42 Browne Harry
43 Dye Arthur
44 Jerry George
45 Howard Albert
46 Smith James T   (baker)

## LAW'S YARD
*From 12 Bridge Street*

1 Thorn John Samuel
2 Purdy Ernest Edward  (firewood dealer)
3 Branham William
4 Moule Miss
5 Groom Robert William
6 Nuccoll James William
7 Chapman William
8 Panton Herbert

Linay's Yard, Church Street.

## LAW'S YARD*
*From 7 High Street*
1  Flagg Mrs
2  Hardy Walton
3  Pearman Horace
4  Loasby Miss
5  Mindham Edward
7  Chapman Mrs
7a Farrow Herbert James
8  Hughes Edward W

## LEACHES YARD
*From 11 Tower Street*
1 Higham Robert
Mansell George A  (printer)

## LINAY'S YARD
*From 27 Church Street*
Murton Walter
Pitt Mrs Clara

## LITTLE CHEQUER
*From 1 Purfleet Place*
1  Girdlestone Edward
2  Doy Thomas
3  Tuck Walter
4  Bulman William

## LINCOLN'S YARD*
*From 9 Purfleet Street*
1  Collins Michael
2  Rix George

## LITTLEPORT STREET
*From Norfolk Street to Gaywood Road*
South side
Duke of Edinburgh PH   (William H Jeffries)
Howard Henry Lewis  (St Katherines)
Elam John (Silverwood)
Curtis Daniel R   (pork butcher)
Ebling Jack  (greengrocer)
*here is Cross Yard*
5  Sizeland George  (fried fish shop)
6  Land Gerald John
7  Peckover Charles  (shopkeeper)
8  Drake Mrs
9  Harvey Frederick Charles  (corn merchant)
*here is Littleport Terrace*
Hob-in-the-Well PH   (John G Church)
North side
Chilvers Brothers  (cycle agents)
2  Merrywest Frederick L  (dairyman)
Bardell Anthony   (Stanley House)
Lift Mrs  (Donovan Yard)
Leader John (Donovan Cottage)
Curtis DR (Donovan House)
Sandringham PH    (Albert L Carpenter)
Hilton Mrs Elsie M (confectioner)
Hilton Herbert  (painter)

On the corner of Littleport Street and Austin Street stood Chilvers (Eastgates Garage & Cycle Works).

## LITTLEPORT STREET (continued)

Withers J  (mangle repairer)
Withers Mrs KM  (midwife)
Braybrooke Miss Lily  (shopkeeper)
Jack David Samson MRCVS
veterinary surgeon  (Eastgates)
*here is Kettle Well Lane*

## LITTLEPORT TERRACE

*From 9 Littleport Street to Paxton Terrace*
### West side

1  Patrick Mrs MA
2  Sayer Mrs
3  Trevor William
4  Howard John Henry
5  Clements Alfred
6  Peck Herbert Victor
7  Colby Mrs
8  Waller Frederick
Trundley Charles (Lindum)
Pettit Charles (Melville House)
Bland William Henry (Darton House)
Parrish Ernest (Lyn Wal)
Herrington Arthur (Glenfern)

Burch Mrs
Howard John
*here is Railway Terrace*

## LOKE ROAD

*From Estuary Road to*
*79 Loke Road extension*
### North side

2 Balls George William
4 Sidgwick Mrs M  (shopkeeper)
6 Overton Robert J
8 Gittens George
10 Kendle Albert
12 White Tom
14 Powley Arthur
16 Baker George William
18 Bocking Henry
*here is North End & North End Yard*
20 Baker Sidney C  (builder)
22 Crowe William
24 Mann Stanley
26 Capps Arthur
28 Barren Alfred
30 Bunn Mrs

## LOKE ROAD (continued)

32 Rudd Charles Walter
34 Leman George
36 Allen William  (shopkeeper)

*here is Lansdowne Street*

38 Davey Saul  (butcher)
40 Gent David
42 Curtis Charles
44 Goodson John
46 Goodson Harry
48 Butcher Miss Mary (shopkeeper)

*here is Birchwood Street*

50 Johnson William J
52 Booth William L  (cars for hire)
54 Barker Joseph
56 Barker Joseph
58 Bunn Thomas G  senior

*here is George Street*

60 Collins Miss F  (shopkeeper)
62 Ollett Henry Charles
64 Corteen Walter S

### South side

*here is Sir Lewis Street*

7 Searle Mrs Ellen  (shopkeeper)
9 Kendle John  (fried fish dealer)
11 Walker Fras. (hairdresser)
13 Leman George  (baker)
15 Jarvis JC
17 Leman George  (grocer & post office)

*here is Cresswell Street*

21 **Bentinck PH  (Albert Booty)**
23 Woods George  (dairyman)
25 Roy Mrs
27 Pottle Alfred
29 Collins Alfred
31 Bunn Thomas G  (fishmonger)

*here is Burkitt Street*

33 Collins William Thomas
35 Laidman George
37 Watling Mrs
39 Burgoyne Mrs
41 Ship Horace Edward

43 Turbett Stewart
45 Burton AP  (carter)
47 Chase Mrs

*here is Brick Yard*

53 Smith Thomas
55 Rose Charles
57  Booth Wilfred
59  Brookes Thomas
61   Burton Albert
63  Merrican Miss
65  Stokoe Thomas R
67 Juniper George Samuel
69 Gamble Mrs
71 Johnson Robert
73 Croucher William S
75 Houke Charles FW

### LOKE ROAD EXTENSION
*From Loke Road to Salter's Road*
### North side

79 Wilson Frank
81 Pegram James Arthur
83 Ward Percy
85 Gazley Horace
87 Canham Charles John
89 Bunton William
91 Reid Mrs
93 —
95 —
97 Titmarsh George
99 Riches George
101 Creek Frederick
103 Frow Henry
105 Patrick Miss Gladys  (teacher of music)
105 Patrick Mrs

*here is Edma Street*

107 Bradford Mrs
109 Newby Arthur
111 Chapman George
113 Drew Robert
115 Massen Sidney

A normal winter's morning on London Road looking from County Court Road. A bus has just left the Millfleet and heads towards Wootton. The library dominates the background.

## LOKE ROAD EXTENSION (continued)

117 Bloye Percy RV (assistant insurance
    superintendent)
121 Cook George W
123 Booty Albert
125 Marshall William
127 Cox Percy Frederick
129 Overland Albert Charles
131 Jackson Frederick
133 Collison Miss (corsetière)
135 Hansford Charles
137 Barrett Herbert
139 —
141 Van Dyke Lionel D
143 Booty Albert
145 —
147 Smith Frederick
149 Tokelove George Henry
151 Alcock Samuel Francis
153 Rogers Miss

155 Drew Ferdinand A
157 Plain Thomas
159 Linford Robert
161 Baker Richard
163 Sparrow Bertie
165 Middleton Bert
167 Garwell John
169 Medwell Ernest

### South side

164 Spragg Miss
162 Jaggs George
160 Lever Arthur Charles
158 Lake Ernest
156 Smith Ernest Thomas
154 Hawkins Henry Thomas
152 Frost Bramwell
150 Roberts HS
148 Youngs Alfred
146 Tunmore Frederick  (insurance agent)
144 Gray Henry Edward

## LOKE ROAD EXTENSION (continued)

142 Browne Walter. Henry  (tailor)
140 Newby William
138 Dix Ernest
136 Nicholas John William
132 Crichton William
130 Ashmore Charles
128 Jones John William
126 Bunn Frederick
124 Stafford Mrs
124 Stafford Edward William  (haulage contractor)
122 Plain Mrs
120 —
118 Rockett Horace
116 Simpson James
114 Cresey Charles
112 Fisher Henry B
110 —
104 Hobson John
102 Williams Ernest
100 Ruckley Gordon William
98 Tyler Edward William
96 Piper James
94 Emms Robert Coates
92 Stevens John Henry
90 —
88 McWilliams Mrs
86 —

**LNER railway sidings**
*See South Lynn environs*

## LONDON ROAD
*From St James' Road to South Gates*
### East side
King's Lynn Infant Welfare Centre
St. James Methodist Chapel
County Court (Percival Armorer Forster, registrar & high bailiff & George Smith, chief clerk)
District Registry of the High Court of Justice
(Percival Armorer Forster, district registrar)
Smith George (County Court House)
*here is County Court Road*
Framingham's Hospital (almshouses)
1 Hayes Mrs
2 Cowley Mrs M  (confectioner)
3 White William  (nurseryman)
4 Barton Francis H   (hairdresser)
5 Wright Jasper James
6 Mendham Wace Lockett
7 Pointer Mrs
8 —
9 Bush William   (builder)
10 Powell Herbert
11 Shaw, Smith & Co  (accountants)
12 Adams Ernest R
12 Ripley Hall (E R Adams, proprietor)
12 East Anglian Entertainments Ltd
*here are Brewery Buildings*
13 King's Lynn Motors Ltd. (motor engineers)
14 Andrews Thomas Henry
15 **Queen's Arms PH   (Alfred William Stratton Hanes)**
King's Lynn Municipal Technical Institute (H M Howard BA director & secretary)
St. James' Council School (boys)
West Norfolk & King's Lynn General Hospital
*here is Hospital Walk*
16 Britannic Assurance Co. Ltd. (Eric Grundy, manager)
17 Fuller Mrs
18 Bloomfield James (greengrocer)
19 Howard Frederick
20 Allflatt William Henry  (dairyman)
21 Sharpin William M
22 Oliver Miss
24 Simkins Mrs
25 Swann Charles Lister
*here are Whitehouse Cottages*

| LONDON ROAD (continued) | 42 Taylor Richard |

## LONDON ROAD (continued)

26 Renaut Bros. (builders)
27 Medd Mrs ME (tobacconist)
28 Giles Frank (greengrocer)
29 Hunt Mrs
30 Claxton Bert
31 Hayes JR & Son (chemists)
*here is Windsor Road*
32 White Mrs ME (newsagent)
33 Owen Miss Miriam (hairdresser)
33 Owen George
34 Green Mrs EMA JP
35 —
36 —
37 Page Miss
38 Slator Alfred. John
39 Hewitt John
40 Clarke Mrs Mahala (apartments)
41 Eydmann Alfred George

42 Taylor Richard
43 Robinson E & Co. (wood trellis makers)
44 Gotobed J Mott (lubricating oil factor)
*here is Gilbert Row*
45 —

### Terrace Lane

1 Simpson RJ
1 Simpson WG (school attendance officer)
———
46 Clarke William Alfred
46 Eastmans Ltd (butchers)
47 Scott Arthur
48 Stibowsky Josef (tailor)
50 Herring Mrs EH (confectioner & post office))
51 Kirby & Son (greengrocers)
52 Kirby George (hairdresser)
53 Logsdail Henry (chemist)
54 Blomfield Thomas F (butcher)

St James Methodist Church and County Court at night in the 1930s.

## LONDON ROAD (continued)

55  Deans A & Sons  (grocers)
56  Mills Ernest Walter
57  Thompson Alfred John
*here is Guanock Place*
59  Plowright FH  (boot repairer)
### West side
60a  **Honest Lawyer PH   (Charles Frederick Nicholls)**
*here is Southgate Street*
60  Daynes George E & Son  (grocers)
61  Mason Harry   (shopkeeper)
62  Medlock Richard
63  Regester Miss E
64  —
65  Smith Mrs
66  Clements Mrs E
67  Fisher John
68  Lemmon Frederick
69  Purser Henry James
70  Carter Joseph  (draper)

71  Wallis George
72  Boulding Robert J
73  Mitchell James Samuel  (dentist)
74  Barker Joseph
75  Davis Albert
76  Pycroft William Nicholas
77  Brown Horace  (monumental mason)
*here is Checker Street*
78  **London Porter House PH (Alfred Barber)**
Berry & Duxson  (boot repairers)
Wesleyan Methodist Church
*here is South Everard Street*
79  Sillett Fred  (motor engineer)
Seapey Hugh Gordon  (monumental mason)
88  Robinson Charles Albert  (draper)
89  Overland John William
90  Roy Ernest Victor
All Saints' Church Room

The statue of Alderman Frederick Savage in London Road at the unveiling on the 15th February 1933 attended by showmen to commemorate his initiative in applying steam power to fair ground machinery.

## LONDON ROAD (continued)

92  Hammill R Caldwell  LDS, RFPS (dental surgeon)
93  Appleby Mrs
94  Morriss Mrs
    *here is North Everard Street*
Roman Catholic Church of St. Mary of the Annunciation
Stokes Rev. Edmund H (The Roman Catholic Rectory)
95  Lavender Miss J  (draper)
96 & 97  Nursing Home
97  Jackson Charles ES  MB, BS Lond, FRCS Eng. (surgeon)
    *here is Valinger's Road*
98  Gates Alex  (dentist)
99  Large Mrs S
100  Otterspoor  Cornelius
101  Batch John William  (poultry dealer)
101a  Seapey William Edward
102  Misson Ronald   (hairdresser)
103  Fuller Frederick  (wireless dealer)
104  Williams Miss
105  Sexton John  MB, BCh, BAO, (physician)
105  Fogarty  MB, BCh, BAO (physician)
105  Fogarty Edmond MB, BCh, BAO, LM Dubl  (physician)

106  Lindsey Charles William
107  Collinson Harry Whalley
108  Blmofield Mrs
109  Walker Mrs EM  (confectioner)
110  Porter David W  (fried fish dealer)
111  Watts George William
112  Harris Henry  (pork butcher)
    *here is Providence Street*
113  Daisley Francis Howard  (confectioner)
114  Dawson Ernest John
115  Howard Frederick W  (butcher)
116  Smith Herbert Goshawk
117 & 118 Pidgeon Frederick  (ironmonger)
119 Bonham & Co  (coal merchants)
121 Easter Henry G  (confectioner)
122 & 123 **Carpenters' Arms PH (Albert Edward A Hastings)**

124 Johnson WH & Sons Ltd  (motor engineers)
125/125/127  Medlock HR   (confectioner)
128 & 129 Pointer LB   (newsagent)
130 Withers Edward Thomas   (cycle store)
    *here is Millfeet Terrace*
Stanley Public Library (CH Senior, librarian)
    *here is War Memorial (Tower Gardens)*

The new Clarke Bros. Garage on Lynn Road in 1936.

## LONG ROW (Highgate)

*From 31 Front Row*

1  Leeder Frederick
2  Overson James
3  Gilbert Clement Edgar
4  Steel William
5  Hudson Albert
6  West Fred
7  Holmes Hiram
8  Knights Albert
9  Wright Arthur
10  Roper Ernest
11  Fulcher Percy
12  Blyth Mrs

## LOWE'S YARD

*From rear of 5 Church Lane*

1  Barnes Walter

## LYNN ROAD♦

*From 161 Gaywood Road to Wootton Road*
### North side

1 Bunkall Eldred  (registrar of births, deaths & vaccination officer)
Anderson Mrs (Victoria Bungalow)
3 Cooper Mrs
5 Osborne George
*here are Victoria Buildings)*
7 Carter Oscar, (shopkeeper)
9 Osborne Harry Southwell
11 Colquhoun Mrs
13 **Diamond Jubilee PH    (W Jordan)**
15 Whittley James
17 Sharman William
19 Thompson Walter
21 Knowles Ernest
23 Gent Mrs
25 Reeve James Stacey
27 Wooll Sydney John
29 **Ship PH    (Charles Avis)**
31 Cobb Henry William  (saddler)

33 Avis Mrs H
35 Mobbs James
37 Smith Albert Edward
39 Whitley Henry William
41 Whitmore Mark   builder)
Richardson Mrs I  (St. Helens)
Whittley Robert (Madgville)
Hewlett John Thomas (Roseville)
Thornington Frank (The Bungalow)
43 Hayes Thomas W
45 Hayes Miss Evelyn  (confectioner)
*here are Harrows Buildings*
47 Mallett Harry   (decorator)
49 Back Charles Henry
53 Richmond Alfred W  (coal merchant)
Shepherd Mrs
Watson Rupert
55 Haywood Mrs
57 Ewen Mrs E
59 Raines James
61  Baker Robert
63 Tovell Charles Frederick
65 Batterham Stephen
67 Bindley Gordon
69  Howell John
71  Tovell James William
73  Empson John
77 Wilson Mrs Mary   (shopkeeper)
79 Thurston William John
81 Cuttell Harold
83 King's Lynn & District Cooperative
   Society Ltd
*here is Wootton Road*
### South side

2  Cross Mrs
4 Towler Mrs W
6 King William Leonard
8 Greeves Harold O
10 Clift Mrs MA SRN  (nurse)
12  Green Miss
14  Mallett Miss
16 Place Miss

## LYNN ROAD♦ (continued)

18 Lake George Walter
20 Ingram Misses
22 Jackson Leonard Wadham
24 Vernon Leslie C
26 Andrew Arthur Banks
28 Rust Miss
30 Pipe Edgar P
32 Browne Joseph J  (electrician)
34 Walker John W
36 Anderson Wallace
38 Rowlett Samuel Edgar
   Moore Walter  (builder)  (Taly-Cafn)
52 Woods Charles William  (boot repairer)
58 Copeman Cornelius Henry
60 Rayner Richard
60a Malt William
62a  Donald William
64 Gunns Mrs
66 Fysh Mrs SM
   Smith Thomas E  (carpenter)
68 Nicholls George S  (blacksmith)
70 Medlock Rd

## MALT ROW♦

*From 341 Wootton Road*

1  Fenn Charles William
2  Wilson Edward
3  Fenn Robert
4  Murrell George
5  Grimmer Albert John
6  Overland Miss
7  Toll Herbert Frederick
8  Blake Ferdinand
9  Seapey John Henry
10  Galey William Samuel
11  Toll John
12  Merrikin Frederick
13  Gore Josiah

## MARKET LANE

*From 37 Chapel Street to*
*Tuesday Market Place*

1  Sutton Alfred
2  Whatford Mrs Rebecca  (wardrobe dealer)

*here is Edward's Yard*

5 Mott Matthew
**Duke's Head Hotel  (tap)**

## MARKET STREET

*From 28 Railway Road to Paradise Parade*
### West side

1  Turner Harry
2  Rasberry Mrs
3  Hunt Mrs
Baptist Sunday School
4  Easter Miss
5  Cassin Richard
6  Musson Arthur  (insurance agent)
7  & 8 Westwood Thomas  (shopkeeper & deputy registrar of marriages for Freebridge Lynn district))
9 **Lord Kelvin PH  (Minnie Maud Stanley)**
10  Self John Robert  (dairyman)
11  Bird Phillip
12  Richardson Miss
Dockerill Percy  (builder)
13  Smyth Albert
14  Jackson Robert William (furniture remover)
14  Jackson Robert William
15  Carter Mrs Sarah Ann
16  Allen Frederick
### North side
25 Emmerson Herbert
23 & 24 Warner H & Son  (heating engineers)
22 Bocking Percy George (picture frame maker)
21 Bocking Percy George
20 Gibson Thomas W

*here is Albion Street*

19 Millatt Edward

18 Smith Henry

Curson Alexander (printer)

Museum & Art Gallery (HE Bocking, curator)

## MARSH LANE♦

*From 209 Wootton Road*

### North side

Griffiths Russell Frederick (Reno)

Elsegood Edward (Edreen)

Miles Edward Thomas (St. Leger)

1 Howard Mrs

2 Rayner Harry

3 Ward Mrs

4 Isbell Charles Edward

5 Massingham John

6 Bunkall George

7 Medlock Mrs

8 Turner Walter. Charles

9 Collison Harry

10 Purvis Alfred

11 Plowright Ernest

12 Howlett David

13 Medwell Miss

### South side

Back Henry

Mayes Frederick Benjamin

Newson Henry F

Leach Jessie Oliver

Sebar Willie

Bird Reginald

Lougher Rupert V (The Retreat)

Coker George (Kemona)

Pounds Leslie (The Glen)

Bensley John

Baker George

Smith Mrs E (The Rest)

Alcock Ralph (Floral)

Rose George (Roselea)

*here is Bevis Way*

Cowley Michael (Glendalough)

Gore Albert Edwin (farmer) (Marsh Lane Farm)

Brown Charles

## MARSHALL STREET

*From 60 Railway Road to Bedford Street*

### West side

Fayers Robert H & Son (joiners - workshop))

1 East Frederick Henry

2 Monument George

3 Fayers Robert H & Son (joiners)

4 Knights Frederick

5 Tabbutt Robert

6 Mumford Charles

### East side

Medwell James & Sons (building contractors) (workshop)

Parks Walter (french polisher)

11 Roome Charles

10 Nelson Herbert

7 Bailey William

8 French William

9 Hall Mrs

## MELBOURNE STREET

*From 13 South Clough Lane*

### East side

35 Tinkler Alfred

33 Guy George

32 Woodward Miss G

31 Lake Miss AC

30 Ransom Mrs G

29 Griffiths Mrs

28 Howard Arthur Ernest

27 Barber John

*here is Russell Place*

26 Frost James

25 Bennell Frederick John

24 Curston Mrs

23 Griffin William

22 Wright Mrs L

By August 1934 the building of new houses for 512 families was well under way at South Lynn. The streets which stretched between Wisbech Road and Saddlebow Road where the construction of these homes took place were (later named) Metcalf, Bunnett, Burney & Hillen Roads and Beloe Crescent. Described in the Lynn News as 'light and airy with gardens front and back - a wonderful change from the condemned houses in Lynn's courts, alleys, lanes and yards - and the rents will be such as a working man can pay.'

## MELBOURNE STREET (continued)

21 Leeder Mrs L
20 Bloy George

### West side

19 Burton Mrs
18 Frost Herbert Ernest
17 Garrod John
16 Humphrey Robert
15 Collison Gaston
14 Starling William
13 Griggs Arthur
12 Watts Bertie E
11 Misson Thomas
10 Plumb William
9 Lord Charles
8 Knights Harry
7 Norris James
6 Claydon Richard
5 Larkman James

4 Browne Mrs HM
3 Lord James Edward
2 Cooper Mrs H
1 Baker Mrs E

## METCALF AVENUE

*From 63 Wisbech Road to*
*56 Saddlebow Road*

### South side

1 Collins Percy
3 Cross Albert
5 Castle Jack
7 West John
9 Taylor Isaac James
11 Auker Harry
13 Collier William
15 Roy Reginald Bertram
17 Taylor Frederick
19 Smith Robert

Miles Square or Miles Court in 1933.

## METCALF AVENUE (continued)

| | |
|---|---|
| 21 Jarvis William | 10 Dean Charles William |
| 23 Stafford Mrs | 12 Holland William |
| 25 Britton John | 14 Goldsmith James |
| 27 Russell Claude C | 16 Catton Ernest |
| 29 Fretwell Victor | 18 Smith John Robert |
| 31 Fox George L | 20 Tuck Sidney A |
| 33 Bather Edward | 22 Sizen Philip |
| 35 Thurston Daniel | 24 Massingham Lewis Earl |
| 37 Skipper Walter | 26 Gamble Harry |
| 39 Hurn Boydll | 28 Vice William Redvers |
| 41 Howard Ernest W | 30 Watson Frederick William |
| 43 Bruce James | 32 Gent Bert Oswald |
| 45 Lubbock George E | 34 Senter Edward Thomas |
| 47 Curry Frederick C | 36 Fysh George Henry |
| **North side** | 38 Smith Arthur |
| 2 Barber Francis | 40 Wright William R |
| 4 Fox Albert | |
| 6 Cobbold Hector | |
| 8 Backham Ernest Edward | |

Miller's Court, Bridge Street in 1933

## METHUEN AVENUE♦

*From 89 Wootton Road*

### North side

Hewett George Cecil H (St. Valentine)
Hawes Alfred (Waldene)
Bull Samuel (Yesanne)
Thurston Frederick (Sunny Dene)
Collins Wilfred John (Maardi)
Hooke Frank Victor (Franmac)
Sizeland Arthur Thomas (Ethlyn)
Chilvers John (Lennox)

### South side

Warren Jasper (Loughworth)
Smith Mrs L. (Angorfa)
Neilson James (Cathcart)
Court Henry Joseph (Selsdon)

### East side

Trundley Frank (The Haven)
Griffiths Mrs A. M. (Llanberis)
Blenkinsop William (Valkyrie)
Claydon Walter. George (Ramleh)
Gazley Walter. (Dunsmuir)
Bates Douglas William (Alumrock)
Mihell James (Southgate)
Dent Horace Alonzo (Lewdene)
Ragless Alfred. George (Sorrento)
Hayes Ernest (Lyndhurst)
Kent Ernest Edward (Marina)

Peachey Burgess (St. Owens)
26 Prior George Reginald
Schofield Frank (Shirley)
Ashton Frederick (Vigympie)
Emerson George (Marlow)
Harris Thomas (Conway)

### West side

Sutterby Cecil Robert (Journey's End)
Sutterby Mrs Amy (dressmaker) ( Journey's End)
Renaut Arthur Charles (Belmont)
Chapman Stanley George (Hemingford)
Gemmell Arthur (Mellford)
Bocking Reginald. George (Evesholm)
Hantori James Ogden (St. Mabyn)
Bennett Frederick John (Ben-ici)
Hanslip John (Ellesmere)
Culley Stephen (Kenworth)
Denman William Marter (Ventnor)
Haigh Albert Henry (Xauen)
Allen Horace (Burpham)
Bloor John (Trentham)
Summers Frank Edgar (Langley)

## MIDLAND CHAMBERS

*See 63 & 64 High Street*

93

Millfleet Terrace in 1933

## MILES'S SQUARE (COURT)*
*From 7 Chapel Street*
2 Stacey James
3 Burch Sidney George
4 Leggett Alfred. James
5 Roper Charles
6 Steel James
7 Hardy John William
8 Dexter Frank
9 Briggs William H
10 Culpitt Edward William
11 Anderson Mrs
12 Mawby Miss
13 Seaman Miss
14 Howard William Charles

## MILLER'S COURT*
*From 9a Bridge Street*
Russell William Arthur
1 Moule Ernest Arthur
2 Cowen Mrs Fanny

## MILL LANE♦
*From 255 Wootton Road*
1 Mansell Rhys
2 Carnell Arthur
2a Barrett Sidney
Long Ernest Alfred (Cringleford)
Oliver Alan (Kozy Kot)
Sharpin George (Nigella)
Mott Herbert D (Alastir)
Allison Elizman John (Gramare)
Wiseman Arthur Francis   (The Hollies)

Starling James (Restavon)
8 Richardson Charles John
9 Regester Frederick
10 Oakey Percy William
Capps Emmanuel William (Kingswood)

## MILLFLEET TERRACE

*From 130 London Road to Stonegate Street*

1 Wilson Augustus Owen  (apartments)
2 Kenney Thomas Edward  (apartments)
3 Dyer Charles Edwin
4 Lawson John William
5 Dixon A & Son   (fried fish dealers)
   Smith George Frederick
6 Goodrum George
7 Senter M & H   (fried fish dealers)
8 Medlock Mrs S
9 Pheasant Frederick
10 Pheasant Frederick John
11 Wilkin John F  (insurance agent)
12 Woodhouse Horace

**Lincoln Tavern   (Evelyn Gittens)**

*here is Vicarage Lane*

14 Newman Mrs MA
15 Spinks Denis Inglebright
16 Whitmore Miss
17 & 18 Beaty Ernest   (fruiterer)
Harpley Mrs Ruth   (confectioner)

## MILLS YARD

*From 13 Sedgeford Lane*

Gilbert Miss
Empson Mrs
Chilvers George
Terelinck John
Fox Sydney
Fickling Mrs
Collison Robert
Richardson Mrs
Rust Ernest

## MILTON AVENUE

*From Elna Tennyson Avenue*

North side

1 Bradfield Mrs AS
Kinchin Howard (Paradise)
Bird Cyril (The Nest)
8 Stringer Lester

10 Young Walter John
12 Bird Reginald Harry
14 Castle Miss EC
16 —
18 Woodford Egerton Robert
20 Hanton Benjamin
22 Stringer Albert Edward
24 Benger Douglas Jack
26 Sherman Miss KF
Hodnett Hubert H (West View)
MacKender Harry C (Joydene)
Fitch Miss MS (Wyncroft)
Algar Leonard (Fonnereau)
38 Phillips Edwin E
40 Willden Dennis A
42 Piper Alfred Stanley
Langley Walter C  (insurance agent) (Eastleigh)

In 1936 it was proposed that a statue of Captain Vancouver be erected opposite the entrance to the house where he was born. This is an artists impression as to how it would look on New Conduit Street

Captain Vancouver's home in New Conduit Street. He was born here in 1757.

## MILTON AVENUE (continued)
### South side
Taylor Edward W (Chalfont)
Folkes Arthur G (Linden Lea)
Hodson Edwin W (Chalfont)
Richardson Walter. (Glenhurst)
Housley Mrs A (Plaza)
Slator Miss (York House)
Holmes Shirley F (Lourdes)
15 Ward Edward George
Thurston Mrs S A (Blackboro')
21 Anderson Basil Ernest
Sexton Archibald S (Hazelwood)
Jolly Cyril Edward (Vectis)
Scott-Richardson George (Harecroft)
Goddard Melton (Glen Ayr)

## MOUNT PLEASANT
*See Regent Street*

## MOUNT STREET
*From 85 Tennyson Road*
### North-west side
1  Smith Robert S
2  Adlam Walter Joseph
3  Brown Mrs
4  Francis John Edward
5  Philpott Bertram Edward
6  Hayden Ernest Alfred

7  Kisby Kenneth
8  Curtis Charles
9  Reddy John Henry

## NELSON STREET
*From St Margaret's Place to Stonegate Street*
### West side
1  Dennick John Iles (coal merchant)
3  Baker George A  (joiner)
*here is Hampton Court*
5 Dennick John I  (coal merchant) (store)
7  Tuffs John Henry
9 King's Lynn & West Norfolk Club
(C A Debenham  (hon sec & treasurer)
11 Freeman Miss HM
13  Rudd Claude Ellis
15 & 17 Mclntosh James W, MB, ChB, FRCS Edin, BSc (physician & surgeon & medical officer of health, to the borough & Port Sanitary Authority & school medical officer)
15 & 17 Mclntosh Mrs Eleanor, CE, MB, BS Lond, MRCS, DPH (physician & surgeon)
15a Tizard Miss
15b Dent Walter Frederick
Mackinder Edwin  (cattle food manufacturer)
19 Bennett John Edwin
Bennett John Lee & Son Ltd.  (corn Merchants)
### East side
2 —
4  Oswell George Richardson
6  Williamson Arthur
8  Ashton Frederick William
10 Tuffs Percy
12 Chapman George
*here is Bagge's Yard*
14  Bath Miss Jane
16  Joplin Robert
18 Cook Frederick

R & A Taylor celebrate George V Silver jubilee in 1935. This business had begun in 1770 - when George lll was celebrating his 10th anniversary on the throne.

| NELSON STREET (continued) | NEW CONDUIT STREET |
|---|---|
| 18 Cook Mrs Emily  (dressmaker) | *From High Street to Baxter's Plain* |
| 20  Barber Ernest Claude Alfred | South west side |
| 22 Howlett James Henry | 1 — |
| 24 Rix James | 2  Page GB  (antique dealer) |
| 26 Allen George | 3  Corporation Electricity Showrooms |
| 28 Witt Frederick George | North east side |
| 30 Winearls Horace G | 5 Piper James & Sons   (hairdressers) |
| 34 Baker George A (joiner) | *here is Burton's Court* |
| 36 George Alfred Henry | 7 Smith Murray   (tailor) |
| | Ladyman JH & Co. Ltd. (grocers) (warehouse) |
| **NELSON TERRACE** | 9 Bunkall Mrs |
| *See Wisbech Road* | 11 Sadler George G |
| | 13  Nicholls William |
| | 15  Dawson George |
| | 16  Pearman Percy Henry |

## NEW CONDUIT STREET (continued)

17  Bowman Sidney
19  Smith Percy Frederick  (hairdresser)
19  Pottle Charles William
Ministry of Labour Employment Exchange
(F Lockwood, manager)
Society of Friends' Meeting House
Infant Welfare Centre
25 Tucker CJ & Co.  (grocers)
Congregational Church
27 Beloe, Mackenzie & Co. (GA Mackenzie)
(solicitors & commissioners for oaths) MacKenzie George Archibald (solicitor & commissioner for oaths, clerk to the Charity trustees & to Cleeves Charity & to Cleeves Education Foundation & clerk to Sugar's Almshouse trustees & hon. Representative of Shipwrecked Fishermen & Mariners' Royal Benevolent Society)
Kiddell Mrs (Conduit House)
Pointer Bros.  (cycle agents)

## NEWLYNN (or NEWLYN)

Newlyn was another area of Lynn which would provide more housing.

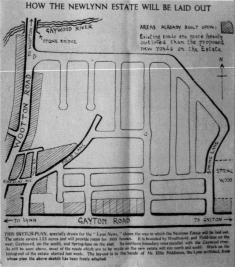

HOW THE NEWLYNN ESTATE WILL BE LAID OUT

THIS SKETCH-PLAN, specially drawn for the "Lynn News," shows the way in which the Newlynn Estate will be laid out. The estate covers 133 acres and will provide room for 800 houses. It is bounded by Wootton-rd. and Field-lane on the west, Gayton-rd. on the south, and Spring-lane on the east. Its northern boundary runs parallel with the Gaywood river. As will be seen above, most of the roads which are to be made on the new estate will run north and south. Work on the laying-out of the estate started last week. The lay-out is in the hands of Mr. Ellis Middleton, the Lynn architect, from whose plan the above sketch has been freely adapted.

## NORFOLK STREET
*From 55 High Street to Littleport Street*
### South side

1  Stephenson, Smart & Co. (accountants)
1  King's Lynn Chamber of Trade
(Stephenson, Smart & Co. sec.)
1  Brice Miss Lilian  (confectioner)
1a Williams Frank  (fruiterer)
2  Labrum RPN  (grocer)
3  Lowe's Restaurant  (hot & cold luncheons)
4  Ely William & Sons  (bakers)
6  Metcalf Roland Alfred. (chemist)
*here is White Lion Court*
6  Johnson George (oil & colour man)
7  Brenner's Bazaar
7a British & Argentine Meat Co. Ltd.  (butchers)
8  Plowright, Pratt & Harbage Ltd.
(ironmongers)
9  Singer Sewing Machine Co. Ltd
9  Breeze Ernest Wilfred
10 Kay's Stores  (grocers)
11 **Fiddamans Hotel  (Herbert W Finbow)**
11 & 12 Nicholls & Campbell Ltd. (wine & spirit merchants)
12 Quick Service Pressing Co. (cleaners)
13 Grosvenor Restaurant (C Winlove-Smith)
*here is Broad Street*
14 Catleughs of Lynn   (outfitters)
15 Lock William & Son Ltd.  (contractors)
17 Lock Charles B    (butcher)

Hugh Raymond Gray (cycle agent) outside his premises at 69 Norfolk Street with his daughter.

## NORFOLK STREET (continued)

18 Hides Alfred    (newsagent)

19 **Bird-in-Hand PH    (Arthur Carnall)**

19 & 20 Davy Bros   (drapers)

21 Sampher Mrs M   (fishmonger)

23 & 24 Kirkland FG    (tailor)

*here is George Yard*

25 & 26 Burman Arthur J   (butcher)

27 Green V   (greengocer)

28 Misson Mrs Sarah   (confectioner)

29 Thacker's Café

30 Easter Mrs Mabel   (tobacconist)

30a Wharton Ernest   (boot repairer)

31 Scotch Home Made Cake Shop (confectioners & caterers)

31 Patfield PW (baker)

*here is Paradise Lane*

32 Smith Mrs Annie L

33 Lincoln Henry James   (grocer)

34 Pank Alfred   (printer)

35 Giles & Isaacson   (drapers)

36 Edmunds Thomas W   (hardware dealer)

36a Bird JC & Son   (printers)

37 Bocking Herbert Victor   (draper)

38 Dawson & Begley   (poulterers)

39 Sun Hotel   Mrs MA Thacker

40 Warrington Percy   tobacconist

41 Southerland Edwards Henry   (butcher)

42 Fitness A   (confectioner)

43 Whitfield George (greengocer)

*here is Rutter's Yard*

44 Blazeby William   (boot maker)

45 Townsend Charles Ltd   (corn merchants)

*here is Railway Road*

49 Tuddenham Mrs Alice   (fried fish shop)

50 Waters Mrs Ada    (confectioner)

51 —

52 East Misses C & A   (confectioners)

53 Alexander Mrs Sarah A   (newsagent)

54 & 55 Roper AH & Co (wholesale drapers)

56 Fay's Polishes Ltd.   (polish producers)

A display of Austin vehicles sold to Lynn Corporation by LE Taylor (145, Norfolk Street).

## NORFOLK STREET (continued)

57  Ash Charles Frederick   (tobacconist)
58  Watson James  (greengrocer)
59  King Frederick George
60  Laws Mrs Christina   (fishmonger)
61  Blunt Joseph C
62  Thurston Ernest Edward  (boot repairer)
64  Pycraft Mrs Maud   (butcher)

*here is Kirby Street*

65 —
66  Green Robert  (wardrobe dealer)
67  Hye Francis D  (shopkeeper)
68  Large Ernest   (hairdresser)
69  Gray Hugh Raymond   (cycle agent)
70  Beaney Edward  (fishmonger)
70a Savage Albert Henry (confectioner)
72  Mitchell James (greengrocer)

*here is Blackfriars Road*

### North side

71  Sizeland Edward
72  Riches William (greengocer)
73  Ouzeman Mrs
75 Limbert John Robert   (fried fish shop)
78 —
79  Freeman Miss
80  Senter John William
81  Heckford William Arthur   (baker)
82  Carman Mrs L

*here are Atto's Passage & Atto's Yard*

King's Lynn & District Working Men's
Co-operative Society (central stores)
92  Oakley Horace  MPS   (chemist)

93  Long Mrs Gladys M   (hardware dealer)
94 East Kenneth H & Co.  (rope
manufacterers)
95  Modern Boot Repairing Co (GT Wicks)
97  Kitchener Mrs R (stationer & post
office)
98  Gamble EB  (outfitter)
99  Thrower George  (furniture dealer)

*here is Bell Yard*

100  Barnes Maurice  (leather merchant)
101  Scupham Charles W   (pork butcher)
102  Smith Albert  (fishmonger)
103  Yate Frederick Alfred.  (butcher)
104 **Norwich Arms PH   (Frank C Baxter)**

*here is California Yard*

104  Cott Bernard W  (baby linen)
105  Thomas Mark George  (butcher)
106  King's Lynn & District Working Men's
Co-operative Society Ltd.  (butchers)
107  Towler John Charles  (hairdresser)

*here is Browning's Yard*

108  Fisher George S   (garage)

*here is Hildon's Yard*

109  Jones EH   (fishmonger)
110  Blaxill FC   (tailor)
111  **Eagle Hotel   (Robert C Lorimer)**
112  Goodson Miss Dorothy  (milliner)
112  Fuller Frederick   (wireless dealer)
113  Valentine Mrs EL   (butcher)
114  Howlett William R   (hosier)

*here is Albert Street*

115  Hayes James Robert  MPS   (chemist)

North Street celebrates in the Silver Jubilee in 1935.

## NORFOLK STREET (continued)

116 Hides William J  (florist)
117 Winter Ernest  (jeweller)
119 Ball Charles M  (baker)
120 Gazley GH  (outfitter)
121 Pearks Dairies Ltd. (provision
    dealers)
122 Johnson Ernest Albert  (china dealer)
123 Melias Ltd.  (grocers)
124 Army & Navy Stores (Stratford's Ltd.)
    (clothiers)
125 Baxter Mrs Alice E  (greengrocer)
126 Hulme Bros  (butchers)
127 Culey John T  (corn merchant)
127a Oswell George R & Son  (printers)
128 Blott John T  (tobacconist)
129 Langford Emerson  (ironmonger)
130 & 131 Wilson  (costumier)
132 **Flower Pot PH  (William C Moore)**
    *here is Chapel Street*
133 Trenowath Arthur Ltd  (drapers)
134 Turner Frederick R  (ladies' hairdresser)

135 Hirst William Stanley  (jeweller)
136 London Central Meat Co. Ltd.  (butchers)
137 Sadler Ernest  (costumier)
138 Smith Alfred & Son  (boot makers)
139 Underwood's  (general drapers)
140 Brooke Mrs Louisa  (china dealer)
141 Donaldson's  (fishmongers)
142 Taylor R & A  (seedsmen)
143 Millett EG & Co. Ltd.  (clothier)
145 Taylor LE (1933) Ltd.  (motor car works)
146 Trenowath Bros.  (drapers)
147 Hares Ernest James  (ironmonger)

### NORTH END
*From Hextable Road to 18 Loke Road*

1  Bunting James
2  Lake George
3  Barker Edward
4  Bunting William
5  Walker Stephen
6  Atkinson Frederick
7  Howard Thomas

## NORTH END (continued)

8 Bowman Frederick
9 Bunting Mrs H
10 Chase Charles

## NORTH END YARD

*From Hextable Road to 18 Loke Road*

1a Smith Mrs
2 Howard George
3 Pitt Albert
4 Senter Miss
5 Goodson Ernest
6 Atkinson HA
7 —
8 —
9 Smith Thomas Henry
10 —
11 Miller Charles
12 Collerson Mrs
13 Bailey James
14 Bunn John
15 Allen Frederick Thomas
16 Earl Frederick
17 Day William
18 Akers Arthur
   Stevens Mrs

## NORTH PLACE*

*From 10 North Street*

1 Fisher Charles
2 Fisher Robert
3 Mayer Hendrikus
4 Auker Ralph
5 Cook Mrs
6 Holden William
8 Hillard Mrs
10 Mann Alfred
11 Holden Mrs

## NORTH STREET*

*From St Ann's Street to 41 Pilot Street*
North side

3 & 5  Southgate Mrs E   (shopkeeper)
7 Johnson Miss E
9 Johnson Gilbert Bernard
   *here is True's Yard*
11  Grange Alfred. Stephen
13  Senter William Thomas
15  Bunting George   (grocer)
17  Collison Sydney
   *here is Watson's Yard*
19  Setchell Robert W
21  Massingham Earl E
23  Marshall Thomas Henry
25  Watts Cyril
27  Petts Mrs Mabel   (confectioner)
   *here is Churchman's Yard*
29  Woods David
31  Roper Mrs
33  Johnson Henry Dexter
35  Bann James
37  Howard Mrs
39  Rye Thomas B

North End Yard

| South side | NORTH EVERARD PLACE |
|---|---|

<table>
<tr><td>

### South side

2 **Dock Hotel** (Emma Elvina Kendle)
4 Raper Mrs S (newsagent)
6 Van Pelt Peter Gerret
8 Wenn A (painter)
10 Bigg Archibald (newsagent)
     *here is North Place*
12 Goodson Miss Mary Ann Elizabeth (grocer)
14 Appleton Frederick
16 Hewit Horace
18 Norton Mrs
     *here is Begley's Yard*
20 Paddy James Hawkins
     *here is Devonshire's Yard*
22 Kirby Arthur
24 Roper George Gunton
     *here is Whitening Yard*
26 Bone John (fried fish shop)
28 Allen John Henry
30 Bennell George A (boot maker)

</td><td>

### NORTH EVERARD PLACE
*From 12 North Everard Street*

1 Bunfield Frederick Henry
2 Pinner Thomas
3 —
4 Ellis Percy Reginald
5 Wales Henry Edward
6 Harper Mrs
7 Wales Herbert S

### NORTH EVERARD STREET
*From 5 South Everard Street to*
*94 London Road*
#### South side

1 Walker Miss MR
2 Beales Miss L (dressmaker)
3 Seapey Hugh Gordon
4 Basham Cyril
5 Smith Robert Sydney
6 Lincoln Reginald
7 Gore Charles

</td></tr>
</table>

North Everard Place in 1953

103

## NORTH EVERARD STREET (continued)

8  Barley Elijah
9  Boorman Edward William (shopkeeper)
10  Greaves Sidney
11  Mason Albert William
12  Holmes John Francis
13  Wilson Mrs Hannah   (shopkeeper)
14  Kirby Charles
15 —
16  Peckover Alfred   (baker)
17  Bell Mrs MG
17a Johnson Clifford
18  Moule Albert James
18a Leake Albert Thomas
19  Hurr Sarnuel
20  Large Alfred

*here is John Street*

21  Bear Alfred J
22  Brockett John

### North side

23  Renaut William
24  Lane William
25  Turner Herbert S
26  Leggett Oswald Isaac
27  Peacock John William
28  Abbey  Herbert Lewis
29  Wilmerson William
Cranfield Bros. Ltd.  (millers)
Giles & Bullen   (haulage contractors)

### OUSE AVENUE
*From Hockham Terrace*
#### East side

1  Rix Mrs
3  Cullen Robert
5  Colby Ernest
7  Ebbs George
9  Saddington James
11  Smith John
13  Allen Newman
15  Suiter Nathaniel
17 Brett Reuben

19 Groom William
21 Skerry Ernest Henry
23 —
25 Wiffen Herbert
27 Skate George William
Youngs Cecil (The Nest)
Starling Percy William (Evelyn House)
Tuffs Herbert Jennings (Sidhurst)

### West side

2  Watson Alfred
4  Vice Abraham
6  Barker Henry
8  Oliver Miss
10 Boughen James William
12  Smith Frederick
14  Bell William Lewis
16  Eagle Jonn Henry
18  Hill George John Robert

### PAGE STAIR LANE
*From Tuesday Market Place*
#### North side

North British & Mercantile Insurance Co.
Finch Jacob & Henry Young  (oil cake merchants)
Eldred William J   (shipwright)
King's Lynn Conservancy Board (Alan G Hawkins, clerk to the board)

#### South side

Hygienic Handy Laundry Ltd
Robinson RCR  (table water manufacturer)
Thompson WH (cardboard box
  manufacturers)

### PARADISE LANE
*From 31 Norfolk Street*

1  Sutton William
2  Burrows George
3  Gale Mrs
4  Daw Cyril George
5  Fall Albert Edward

View of the Majestic from Paradise Parade. The Athaeneum has been demolished ready for the building of the new Post Office

## PARADISE PARADE
*From Baxter's Plain*
*here is Broad Street*

1 Scaife Eric (egg depot)
1 Marshall Alan S (tailor)
2 British oil & Cake Mills Ltd (seed crushers)
3 County of Norfolk (western division) Weights & Measures Office
4 Murdin Edward ACIS, FCTS, CFTD (business training college)
4 Carnell & White (chartered architects)
4 Collison Walter (corn merchant)
5 Crome & Akers (printers)
6 Help-One-Another Society (GE Parker, sec)
7 Gotobed & Ayres, egg depot
7 Jubey Silas & Co (electricians)
Bond & Easter (auctioneers)
Cattle Market & Auction Mart
(S Tweedy, collector)

Barclays Bank Ltd. (T Blunt, manager)
Cook Harry M & Son (hay merchants)
Vynne & Everett Ltd. (maltsters)

## PARADISE ROAD
*Blackfriars Street to Paradise Parade*

## PARK AVENUE
*From 85 Tennyson Road*
*to 33 Avenue Road*
### North side
1 Lockwood Frank
3 Tassell Reginald W
5 Barton Oliver L
7 Chamberlain George Henry James
9 Matthews Mrs
11 Allen Harry James JP
13 Stevens John Henry
15 Cartwright Marshall

## PARK AVENUE (continued)

17 Barnes Miss
19 Clarke Arthur John
21 Bremner Bernard E
23 Bone George
25 Beckett James B
27 Hamilton John H
29 Wright John William
31 Southgate William
33 Newton Arthur

30 Pilot Street - home to George William Franklin, dairyman.

### East side

53 Lock Stephen Henry
55 Arnold Mrs
57 Large George
59 Hodd William Jefferson
61 Oliver Edward JB
69 Steward Edgar Albert

### South side

2 Wilson Ernest
4 Goodwin Mrs H
6 Marston Misses
8 —
10 Ellison John Durrant
12 Cooper John B
14 Fox Albert Ernest
16 Howard Ernest
18 Broad Edgar
20 Winter Thomas Frederick H
22 Mobbs Arthur William George
24 Smith Ernest B
26 Riley Harry William
28 Warrington Mrs
30 Francis Joseph E
32 Dunn Robert
34 —
36 Smith Misses Matilda & Emma
38 Easter Henry George
40 Higson Frank Augustine

### PAXTON TERRACE
*From 28 Blackfriars Road to 7 Wyatt Street*

### South side

Hewitt Francis (Kenilworth)
Richardson John (Dover Cottage)
Pask John (Glan Conway)
Youngs William Thomas (Arrow Thwaite)
Henry Frederick (Claremont)
          *here is a passage to Reid Street*
6 Plain Mrs
7 Squier Albert Breeze
21 Errington Robert William
20 Docking Frederick Percy   (hairdresser)

## PAXTON TERRACE (continued)

19 Fysh Mrs
18 Mann Edward George Cecil
17 Howard William
16 Enefer Henry
*here is a passage to Dilke Street*
15 Dack William Alfred
14 Arminger Donald
13 Franklin Alfred
12 Bailey John
11 Stacy Mrs
10 Grief Richard
9 Catton Oswald Fountain
8 Keepe Bertie Robert
North side
St. James' Council School (girls)

## PAYNE'S COURT
*From 10 Church Street*

1 Rye Tom
2 Grummett George
3 Rye Dick
4 Allen Arthur Edward
5 Rumble Fred
6 Reeve George Frederick
7 Deper Frederick Thomas
8 Flight Harry
9 Simpson Charles Warren

## PILOT STREET
*From Chapel Lane to Hextable Road*
East side

6 —
8 Sharpin Charles William   (butcher)
10 Ward James
12 Irwin Miss F   (confectioner)
*here is Hart's Yard*
14 Foster Frederick
16 Barking Reginald
18 Jarvis Frederick
*here is Bird's Yard*
20 Howlett George William (shopkeeper)

22 Wilkin John
24 Howard Thomas
26 Chase Samuel (shopkeeper)
28 Bailey Walter   (fried fish shop)
30 Franklin George William  (dairyman)
*here is Bardell's Yard*
32 Benefer WJ   (shrimper)
34 Watson Walter
36 **Fisherman's Arms PH   (Abel Garnett)**
38 Roberts T
*here is Hanwell's Yard*
40 Hornigold Mrs
42 Bowen William
Wesleyan North End Mission
46 Howard Thomas J
48 Mills William
**Pilot Street Yard**
24 Gray Herbert

———

50 Chase John
52 **Fisherman's Return PH   (Thomas Barnard)**
*here is dock line railway crossing*
54 **Tilden Smith PH   (Stephen Rake)**
*here is Hextable Road*
West side

1 Norris George
3 Norris Jacob
5 Sharpin Mrs
7 Lemmon George
9 Bailey Mrs
11 Howard Robert
13 Harwood John
15 Clow Sidney William
17 Anderson Samuel
19 Lambert Alfred
St. Nicholas' (Church of England) Schools (boys & mixed)
29 Youngman Hinderikus
*here is Half Moon Yard*
31 Goodson Joseph

## PILOT STREET (continued)

35 Bull John   (baker)
*here is North Street*
41 Benefer Thomas (shopkeeper)
43 Gordon Charles
45 Sizen Edwin Robert
47 Rippingill John
*here is Allen's Yard*
49 Allen Alfred Albert
*here is dock line railway crossing*

### PILOT STREET YARD
*See Pilot Street*

### PLEASANT ROW
*From 2 Windsor Road*
#### East side
1 Turner Harry
2 Hawkins Mrs E
3 Carter Mrs LI
4 Barkworth George William Alex
5 Lucas William
6 Elsegood Lewis
7 Neal William
8 Lake George
9 Todd John
10 Simpole Mrs
11 Jary William Ernest John
12 Chilvers Amos
13 Dawes William Barr
14 Adderson William Henry
15 Clift Mrs H
#### West side
16 Cave Harry
17 Featherby Mrs S
18 Lake Henry
19 Bunting Redvers Henry
20 Hardy Mrs AL
21 White Leonard William
22 Greff Mrs AE
23 Greff Leslie  (insurance agent)
23 Greff Herbert Sidney

24 Flowers William Robert
25 Marsters Horace
26 Thomas Edward
27 Curston Herbert Arthur
28 Kendle Philip
29 Wilkin George
30 Chesson Mrs
31 Reynolds Sydney

### PLOUGHWRIGHTS YARD
*From 13 Friars Street*
Painter George Alex
Oakes Mrs S
Rye Ernest Edward

### PORTLAND PLACE
*From 45 Wisbech Road*
*to Lancaster Terrace*
#### North side
1 Smith Robert
2 Cullen George
3 Large Fred
4 Smith Ernest William
5 Paterson James
6 Appleton John
7 Walker George W   (dairyman)
8 Benstead Simeon
*here is Langham Street & Hockham Street*
#### South side
7 Figgis Mrs AM
8 Thurlow Mrs G
9 Fisher Alfred George
10 Hart William Richard

### PORTLAND STREET
*From Blackfriars Road to 40 Railway Road*
#### South side
2 Morris Edwin
3 Marshall James
4 Marsh Mrs
5 Stammers Henry James
6 Ives Miss

Picture taken from the top of the new Montague Burton's looking towards the river. The cleared area on the right is the site of the new Scott's warehouse. In the background is the new Vynne and Everitt silo, the Custom House is also visible.

## PORTLAND STREET (continued)

7   Balding's Commercial Hotel (Mrs LH Beckerton)

### West side

8   Towers Mrs FW  (boarding house)
9   Samson & Anderson   (auctioneers)
9   Anderson AA   (notary public)
10  East Anglian Grain Co. Ltd.
10  Wilson Henry JT
11  Tichbon Mrs A  (boarding house)
12  Fitt Mrs SA   (boarding house)
13  Sadler Ernest
14  Barnes Mrs Florence  (boarding house)
15  Jackson Miss EM  (private nurse's home)
16  Parson Charles
17  Houldridge Leslie
18  Luke Miss Edith ALAM (teacher of music)
19  Collinson Misses

## PRIORY LANE

*From 19 Church Street to*
*St. Margaret's Place*

### South side

1   Wright William
3   Gaskin Mrs AEF
4   Woods Alfred. George
5   Eke Mrs H
6   Sheppardson Thomas Samuel  (chimney sweep)
7   Howard  William Edward
8   Howard Benjamin
9   Drew John Luke
10  Lacey William Edward

### North side

12  Granger Arthur Henry
13  Meggitt Arthur B
14  Crook Charles James
15  Wakefield Robert William
15a Hawkins Mrs Martha

The Purfleet in 1933. The Corporation was at last considering covering in the open sewer that was the Purfleet The properties on the right were about to be demolished to make way for the new Scott's warehouse. The Purfleet is still open today but the water is a lot cleaner!

## PRIORY LANE (continued)
16  Allen Mrs Emily
17  Knowles Herbert John
18  Yallop Horace Frederick
19  Barnes Leonard
20  Ellis Frederick Spencer

## PROVIDENCE STREET
*From 112 London Road to*
*Coronation Square*
### South side
*here is Begley's Yard*
*here are Daisley's Buildings*
2 Wright Robert Charles  (dairyman)
3 Woodhouse John
*here is Harrods Yard*

4  Catton Mrs AE
5  Ess George
*here is East Anglia Place*
6  Williamson Mrs L
7  Bond Thomas Henry
8  Colby Harold
*here is Grummet's Yard*
9  Skerritt Mrs
10  Hewlett Alfred Edward
11  Isle George
12  Gamble John
*here is Colby's Yard*
All Saints' Church
### North side
*here is Vicarage Lane*
Stolham William (Gwydir Cottage)
13  Dorman Frederick William
14  Fitness Albert Edward
*here is Chadwick Street*
15  Willson John  (dairyman)
16  Aldridge Gilbert E
17  Simpson Mrs A & Sons  (shopkeepers)
18  Soden Tom
19  Spinks Frederick William
20  Page Elijah
21  Bridges Frederick Bell
22  —
23  Dawes Frank
24  Shickle Henry
25  Dorman James Walter
26  Simpson James
27  Brookbank Miss
28  Harris James
*here is Hillington Square*
29  Wagge Frank B  (grocer
30  Hall Herbert John
31  Langford James William (shopkeeper)
32  Holgate Robert
33  Shaw Mrs Emily
34  Daisley Miss Martha Ann  (grocer)
35  Plowright Mrs M
36  **Mariners' Compass PH**  (George Bocking)

Purfleet Street looking east towards High Street/New Conduit Street junction.

## PUMP YARD
*From Vicarage Lane*
1 English Albert Edward
2 Curson Mrs
3 Withers Mrs
4 Stephenson Alec

## PURDY'S COURT
*See 84a High Street*

## PURFLEET PLACE
*From 1 Queen Street to King Staith Square*
Cockle & Mack  (oil cake merchants)
*here is Little Checker*
1 Tidd Thomas
2 Burton Benjamin John
3 Prior William

## PURFLEET QUAY
*From King Street*
Custom House (H Gibbons, surveyor of
customs & excise)
Peatling Thomas & Sons Ltd.
(bonding & blending vaults)
British Legion Club (H Ebetts, sec)
Post Office Engineering Dept. (HD Sursham &
WJ Coe, inspectors)  (works)
Walker George M.  (wool merchant)
Blowfield & Watson  (wholesale
confectioners)

## PURFLEET STREET
*From 97 High Street to 2 King Street*
### North side
1, 2, 3 & 4 Scott & Son (King's Lynn) Ltd.
(carpet manufacturers)
5 **Central PH  (Priscilla Chilvers)**
6 Burton Frederick & Son   (cutlers)
7 Burton Mrs Harriet E  (shopkeeper)
*here is Exley's Yard*
8 Cook George  (engineer)
*here is Lincoln's Yard*

9  Nicholls Albert
11 Pegg Mrs
West Norfolk & King's Lynn Newspaper Co.
Ltd. (printers & publishers)
15  Winlove Charles (cabinet  maker)
### South side
16 —
17  Winlove Charles  (cabinet maker, workshop)
18  Giles Alfred
19  Stokeley Arthur  (watch maker)
20  Foreman Robert William  (boot repairer)
21  Hart Walter
22  Weldrick Mrs
*here is Blott's Yard*
25  Pickard George  (fried fish shop)
26  Simper William A
27  Giddens John  (butcher)
28  Brown Francis William
28a Thorn William
29  Regester John William  (baker)
30  Hornigold Charles
31  Dale Frederick & Son  (pork butchers)
32  Hygienic Handy Laundry Ltd.
(receiving office)
32 Hornigold Miss Grace Freda (tobacconist)

## QUAKER'S YARD
*From Baptist Chapel Yard*
8  Ely Alfred. John
7  Collinson Frank
6  Russell Mrs

## QUEEN STREET
*From Purfleet Place to*
*St. Margaret's Place*
### West side
1 Smith William
3 Herring Mrs
5 Larkman William James
7 Jackson Mrs Mary E  (shopkeeper)
9 Fenton Squire
11 Kendle Philip

## QUEEN STREET (continued)

13 Union Jack PH   (George Baker Potter)
15 Blaxill Frederick Charles

*here is King Staith Lane*

17 Page Christopher T   (boarding house)
19 Leake Henry & Son Ltd.   (oil cake manufacturers)   (offices)
21 Brown Frederick James

*here is Crown Yard*

23 Leigh Charles S
25 Allen Mrs Maud   (boarding house)
27 —
29 —
31 Powley Miss Margaret   (school)
31a Clarke Miss M   (masseuse)
33 Thrower Robert W

*here is College Lane*

### East side

10 & 12 Leake Henry & Son Ltd   (oil cake factory)

*here is Baker Lane*

14 Sizeland Matthew   (apartments)
16 Miller Mrs H
18 Hastings Nicholas Samuel
20 Blade Robert
22 Brice Edgar Percival
24 —
26 Dorer Arthur
28 & 30 Adams Percy George   (general merchant)
32 Drew Mrs Martha   (wardrobe dealer)

*here is Bone's Yard*

Burkitt's Almshouses
46 Targett Mrs Alice   (boarding house)

## QUEEN'S AVENUE

*From Wisbech Road*

### North side

1  White Thomas William
2  Humphrey Robert
3  Skerritt Ambrose
4  Freeman Thomas William

5  Fuller Arthur
6  Drew Robert
7  Elms Mrs F
8  Alexander William Frederick
9  Bloomfield Thomas
   Neal Albert (Antigua)
   Anderson Thomas P (Miranda)
   Steward Sidney S  (Norvic)
   Warren Jasper (The Firs)
   Pidgeon Harry A  (Rivers Dale)
   Dexter Francis S (Pearl Villa)
   Turner Herbert James (Myrtle Villa)
   Pooley John (Mercedes Villa)
   Herring Mrs (St. Elmo)
   Vivian Charles Ennis (The Ollands)
   Abbott Michael M (Harbour View)

### South side

Rowe Walter  (The Thrang)
2a Ramm Mrs A G
Holland Mrs (Holland House)
Stokes Thomas William (Pansy Villa)
Peart Russell C. (Jesmond Dene)
Brown William (Ivy Dene)
Hipkin George E (Holly Dene)
Doughty Albert  (insurance agent) (Holly Dene)
White John Thomas (Hignam Villa)
Bunn Edgly Richard (Tynymaes)
Spurling William (Ventnor Villa)
Vipan Robert M (The Neuk)
Worrell A H  (Clenis Dale)
Medlock John (Homelands)
Mann William George (Iris Villa)
Craske Frederick G *(Maud Villa)*
Egan Joseph (Bryn-y-mor Cottage)
Hollis Cubit John (Woolscott)
Dawson Harry H  (St. Leonard's)
Hipkin Benjamin (Mayville)
Gathercole Frank (Bankside)
Corston Robert Henry (Riverside)

Railway Passage 1934. This provided a short cut between Railway Road and Austin Street.

## RABY AVENUE
*From 169 Loke Road (extension)*
*to Salter's Road*
### South side
1 Crome Robert Edward
2 Jex Arthur John
3 Hooks Robert
4 Pegg George William
5 Bailey William
6 Jolley Joseph
7 Mayes Frederick
8 Roberts Mrs
9 Oxbury Edward
10 Miles Albert
11 Marshall William John
12 Anderson Ernest Arthur
### North side
*here is Smith Avenue*

## RAILWAY COTTAGES
*See Hardwick Road*

## RAILWAY PASSAGE
*From 31 Austin Street to 92 Norfolk Street*
### West side
9 Curson Mrs S
10 Morley Mrs
11 Finney Alfred
12 Page Edward Charles
13 Rudd Miss
Trew GB (draper)
### East side
1 Winterton Benjamin
2 Brookes Mrs
3 Sands William John
4 Cannell William
5 Barnaby Mrs
6 Curtis Fred
7 Ransom Ambrose

## RAILWAY ROAD
*From 45 Norfolk Street*
### West side
1 Spreckley G
2 **Barley Mow PH (Frank Dickerson)**
3 Medwell James & Sons (building contractors)
4 Smith James
5 Stalham Bertie
6 & 7 Gore William & Sons (motor engineers)
8 Malt James
9 —
10 Keen Walter N (sign writer)
11 & 12 Dey David S (music dealer)
13 Wain Miss Florence (confectioner)
14 **Stanley Arms PH (Eric Hawksley)**
*here is Albion Street*
15 —
16 Waters Edward J
17 Colman Ernest Edward LRLBA (chartered architect)

114

All that is left of WE Pickering's (tailor) shop in Railway Road after a fire in 1934. Co-incidentally he had suffered a fire at his Blackfriars Road shop exactly 25 years before.

| RAILWAY ROAD (continued) | East side |
|---|---|
| 18 19 & 20  Cox J & Sons  (cycle dealers) | Foreman A F & Sons  (undertakers) |
| 21  Smith Bros  (saddlers) | Popkiss  C & V  (upholsterers) |
| 22 & 23 Frost Thomas Asa  (clothier) | 33 Hilton E  (wireless engineer) |
| 24  Crawford John R | *here is Waterloo Street* |
| 25  Galt Thomas James (chemist) | 34  Eyles George F  (dentist) |
| 26  Johnson Benjamin William  (plumber) | 36  Radford Walter  (cattle dealer) |
| Trinity United Methodist Church | 37  Gibbons Mrs BA |
| 27  Pickering WE  (tailor) | 38  Whittaker Frank  (plasterer) |
| 28  Massingham Miss | 39  Croad Miss |
| 29  Emmerson Herbert  (antique dealer) | *here is Portland Street* |
| *here is Market Street* | 40  Gee Thomas  (hairdresser) |
| 30  Turner Henry M  (boot repairer) | 41  Drew Ernest John  (dentist) |
| 31 Dales Hugh | 42  Chapman Henry |
| 31 Dales Mrs Mildred  (registry office) | 43  Beaty George |
| Independent Order of Oddfellows (Manchester | 44  Fox John |
| Unity) Friendly Society (AA Anderson, | 45  Tilson Mrs |
| Prov.CS) | 46  Colman Mrs |
| Oddfellows' Institute (Henry C Ollett, sec) | 47  Oakes Herbert Harold  (decorator) |
|  | 48  Hamson Mrs S  (hairdresser) |
|  | *here is Wellesley Street* |

## RAILWAY ROAD (continued)

49 —
50 —
51  Sharp Mrs G. (shopkeeper)
52  Gates Mrs
53  Fayers Charles
54  Smith Alfred. J
55  Mears Mrs EA   (fishmonger)
56  Smalls Hubert   (basket maker)
*here is Stanley Street*
57  Goodson Thomas
58  Smith Martin
59a  Holman AF (monumental mason)
59  Johnson Mrs BM
60  Stinton Frank
*here is Marshall Street*
**Crystal Palace PH   (Henry Marwood)**
63 & 64 Dye C & Co. (stationers)
Tuddenham Mrs A (Plemont House)

### RAILWAY TERRACE
*From Littleport Terrace*
### North side
1  Wandford Mrs
2  Miles Harry
3  Handcock Harry
4  Greggs Mrs
5  Juby Henry
6  Barrett John Edward
7 Cullum Miss FS

### RAVENSHAW'S YARD*
*From 25 Chapel Street*
1  Sainty John Robert
2  Wilfred William
3  Franklin Cyril Ivy
Alexander Richard William (cabinet maker)
Burton Arthur Page  (cartage contractor)
Back Alfred  (upholsterer)
Langley J  (joinery manufacturer
Gawthorpe Joseph (Holyoake House)

### REGENT PLACE
*From 55 St James' Street to Regent Street*
### East side
1  Hornigold Frederick
2  Collison Frederick
3  Ellis Alfred
4  Seaman Benjamin George
5  Leaford Miss A
6  Herrell Frank
7  Clark John James
8  Bone Mrs
9  Barrett Edmund
10 —
### West side
11  Sheldrick Mrs MFJ
12  Thurston Frederick

### REGENT STREET
*From 21 South Clough Lane to*
*10 Regent Place*
### East side
Collison Robert   (coal merchant)

**Mount Pleasant**
1  Wiffen George
2  Yallop Mrs
3  Wells Miss
4  Reeder Arthur Edward
———
13 Maxey Frederick
12 Cotton Percy Robert Victor
11  Butcher Richard V
10 West George
9 Soame Charles
8 Franklin Arthur John
7 Rackham Mrs
6 Dack Horace William
5a Drew William James
5  Dowdy Mrs
4 Doy William James
3 Baker Ernest
2 Wilson Leonard Stanley

## REGENT STREET (continued)
Payne Sidney Ernest
### West side
5 Boldero George
6 Butcher Thomas
7 Wenn Mrs M
8 Seaman Mrs E
19 Clements Albert Edward
20 Goate Charles
21 Isbill Mrs
22 Drew Mrs S
23 Cox Henry William
24 —
25 Moy Ernest Albert
26 Fysh Walter George
27 Rayner Joseph
28 Bullman Bert
29 Watkins Mrs
*here is Whincop Street*

## REID STREET
*From 5 Coburg Street*
### East side
1 Wall Mrs
2 Wadlow William
3 Howard Reginald George
4 Chilvers William Percy
### West side
5 Docking Frederick Reginald
6 Skate Albert
7 Baker Mrs H

## RIVER LANE♦
*From 5 Wootton Road*
Mobbs Alfred
*here is Bishops Terrace*
1 Whittley James senior
2 Fysh Frederick
3 Crisp George
4 West Reginald
Newby Stanley Roger (Toorak)
Mason Wilfred (Tidebrook)

Lemmon Arthur (Bishops Lynn)
Frost Walter. William (Holyoake)
Bailey Albert Arthur (Helensburgh)
Jackson Frederick (Fremador)
Partington Henry (Thurlstone)
Bates Thomas (Riverside)
Whittred Reginald Victor (Northdene)
Gibbons James Charles (Brambledene)
Peck Frederick (Cleedale)
Busham Cyril Frederick (Dorcyl)
Batterbee Misses (Neaton)
Hansom Charles (Gaylyn)
Ransom Mrs (Avondale)
Peacock Hubert R (Somersby)
Hazelwood Leslie Edward (Eureka)
Scott Cecil (Rosebud)
Rose John William (Homelea)
Taylor George Alfred (Cambria)
Irwin Charles M (St. Michael)
Kirby Frederick Charles (Fremar)
Wilkinson Eric F (Stow Cottage)
Chapman George (Norton)
Jackson Robert William (Karober)
Bowers Arthur S (Stelmiar)
Fysh Robert (Robnell)

## RIVERSIDE♦
*From 201 Wootton Road*
Moore Leonard (Olcote)
Blott John (Suffield)
Coston Edward Albert
Griffin Albert (Beresford)
Marshall George Henry (Aldersbrook)
Lovick Herbert (Lemona)
Goodman William John (Antonette)
Morris Mrs M (Altona)

## ROBERT STREET*

*From 4 Thomas Street to William Street*

1  Soffley William G
2  Butcher Francis George
4  Chaplin Mrs
5  Fysh Henry
7  Smith Charles

*here is Edward Street*

Newham Bros.   (shoeing smiths)

## ROSEBERY AVENUE♦

*From 60 Wootton Road to Field Road*

### South side

1  Garner Edward
2  Gardiner Joseph
3  Smith Wilfred C
4  Coe Walter. John
5  Mitchell William Robert
6  Wiseman Arthur
7  Jackson William German
8  Macdonald William Douglas
9  Leeder Henry
10  Reeve Henry
11  Browne George
12  Gamble Mrs A
13  Easton Mrs
14  Baldwin George Charles
15  Edwards Leslie F
16  Grant Clarence V
17  Fillenham Sidney
18  Needham Cyril Olaf

### North side

19  Fayers Victor Frederick
20  Mitchell Sidney
21  Marshall Edward
22  Lake Frederick
23  Woods James N
24  Triance Ernest
25  Dorman William B
26  Smith Joseph
Burlingham Joseph Sturge (Morningside)
Parks Miss Dorothy   (confectioner

## RUSSELL PLACE

*From 27 Melbourne Street*

1  Harris George Robert
2  Bouch Frank E
3  Laws George
4  Sheen Henry
5  Tuck Mrs
6  Yate John
7  Clarke Mrs J
8  Hitchcock Harry
9  Snelling Leslie
10  Franklin Harry

## RUSSELL STREET

*From 27 Exton's Road to Graham Street*

1  Jackson Mrs H
2  Rolph Herbert Edward
3  Latus Alfred Gibson
4  Hodges Alfred
5  Allen George
6  Parlett Miss CA
7  Fuller Miss Lucy
8  Wilson Andrew William

## RUTTER'S YARD

*From 43 Norfolk Street*

1  Smith Mrs J
2  Wiles Mrs RC
3  Wiles Edward Victor

## SADDLEBOW

*From Saddlebow Road*

Stacey John (Halfway House, High Road)
Rayner George (1 High Road)
Driver William (2 High Road)
Doubleday E (3 High Road)
Lambert WW (4 High Road)
Parris James H  (dairyman)  (High Road)
Moses William (farmer) (Saddlebow House)
Buck Walter   (market gardener)
Bush John Thomas
Eagleton Robert (farmer)

## SADDLEBOW (continued)

Wilson Arthur (farmer)

**Bull Inn (Ernest Riddleston)**

Batterham William (Willow Farm)

Pank AE & Son (nurserymen)

Gagen Daniel (fruit grower)

Bock Alfred (market gardener) (Orchard House)

Stanger Frederick

S Bracey & W Wells (market gardeners)

St. Helen's Church

Green Harry (Rose Cottage)

Gore Mrs Frances W (dairy farmer)

### SADDLEBOW ROAD

*From Wisbech Road*

### East side

### Council Houses

1 Holmes George

2 Bone Arthur George

3 Suiter William

4 Bailey Ernest

5 Briers Gordon

6 Cowen James

7 Flight Harry

8 Yate Arthur

9 Burton Wilfrid G

10 —

11 Juby Sydney A

12 Sampson Wilfred

13 Gore Thomas S

14 Bird Albert Charles

15 Smart Arthur A

16 Ellis Albert G

17 Richardson Redvers G

18 Burton George E

19 Rasberry Herbert

20 Walker Harry

_____

41 Harvey Mrs B

40 Green Mrs FH

39 Jackson John Moore

38 Panton William Joseph

37 Greenfield Charles Bridger

36 Webb Percy

35 Eke Joseph

34 Taylor Thomas

33 Shirley Edmund Francis

32 Green Alfred

31 Quinsee Edwin Thomas

30 Lake Robert

29 Tilson Thomas William

Basham Frederick (Fern Villa)

Major Frederick (Laurel Villa)

26 Grief George

25 Westlake Sydney

24 Day Joseph

23 Peckover Arthur

22 Stringer Albert Edward

21 Cross Fred

*here is Kitchener Street*

20 Johnson John Joseph

19 Sayer Ernest Harrison

18 Duxson Richard

17 Denny Mrs MA

16 Smith Thomas William

15 Barnard James

14 Dexter Henry

13 Fenn Herbert John

12 Ebling Thomas

11 Cuthbert Frederick John

10 Raby Mrs

9 Eke Mrs

8 Hannam George William

7 Draycott Mrs VA

6 Jenkins Frederick George

5 Newell Mrs

4 Norris George Leslie

3 Reed Frederick George Charles

2 Clitheroe William

1 Watts Bernard

West Norfolk Farmers' Manure & Chemical Co-operative Co. Ltd.

Tice Herbert Richard (Field House)

## SADDLEBOW ROAD (continued)

Copeman William (Westfield)
Peacock Charles William
Tice Herbert William (Bridge Cottage)
Case Miss (Nar House)

### Bardell's Terrace

2 Fitness Samuel
3 Gray William Alex
4 Jarvis Charles
4 Jarvis Miss Dorothy   (dressmaker)
5 Smith Stanley
6 Bell William Thomas
7 Neave Walter
8 Cole Henry James

### St Michael's Terrace

Skerry John William (Rosemary)
Stoakley Edward Arthur (West Haven)
Farmer Joseph William (West Donn)
Knight Ernest Albert (Bowthorpe)
5 Lake George
6 Richardson Alex
7 Taylor John
8 Edmonds Miss EG
9 Weller William John
10 Skillings Edmund
11 Thompson Alfred
12 Bell William

### Southfield Terrace

1 Moy Victor George
2 Neeves Frederick
3 Clark Robert Ernest
4 Bettinson Arthur

———

St. Michael & All Angels' Church
St. Michael's  (C of E) School (mixed)

### Cornwall Terrace

18 Jennings Rd. Philip
17 Twiddy John Howard
16 Wright William
15 Bridges Miss
14 Smith Clifford William G   (shopkeeper)
*here is Sydney Terrace*

Sayer Arthur (Scales How)
Clarke Albert (Kenmure)
10 Pitcher William
Cox Sydney (Egremont House)
Watson Albert Ernest (Durham House)
Pickering Joseph (Coronation House)
Pitcher Arthur (Pretoria House)
Foreman Arthur F (Gledhow House)
Breeze Simon Albert (Verdun House)
Easto William (Ystrad)
Ebling Arthur Walter (Culverthorpe)
Richardson Thomas (Jesmond House)
Pank Alfred S (Everard House)

**Station Hotel   (Walter W Stangroom)**

### Jubilee Terrace

1 Bush Robert George
2 Bush John William
3 Jones Walter William
4 Crowe John
5 King Frank
6 Hammond Robert

———

Melton Robert W (cartage contractor)

## West side

Ellis Charles (Robinville)
Gore George William (Rosedale)
Skerry Ernest E (Trix Villa)
Morris John E (Veronica)
Leech Jesse O (Staplehurst)
Lee Walter Thomas W (Margaret)
Green Reginald (Tregonwell)
Goat Reginald G (Ravenswood)
Thurston John V (Selwyn)
Fairhead Simeon (Alsatian)
Petherbridge William Charles (Maryville)
44 Ransom Frederick C
46 Ashby Edward
48 Lambert Denton Thomas
50 Harrod Cyril
52 Reeve William
54 Capps Frederick George
*here is Metcalf Avenue*

In 1936 the dock lock-up was set for demolition. Last used in around 1916 it had been used to house drunken sailors or even obstreperous brawling locals. It was next door to the dock dining rooms on St Ann's Fort. No.6 had been the Booth residence up to the 1920s.

## SADDLEBOW ROAD (continued)

56 Ebbs Cyril G
58 Oughton John W
60 Ruhms George E
62 Garrard Frederick W
*here is Bunnett Avenue*
64 Smith Glen B
66 Powell William James
South Lynn Station (Midland &
Great Northern Joint Railway)
(Fred Shirley, station master)
The King's Lynn Beet Sugar Factory Ltd.
Eastern General Transport Co. Ltd.
(haulage contractors)

## SADDLETON'S YARD*
*From 13 All Saints Street*
1 Holmes George
2 Cooper George William

## ST ANDREW'S YARD
*From 4 Stonegate Street*

## ST. ANN'S FORT
*From St Ann's Street*
### North side
7 Southgate Bros (grocers, & post office)
3 Southgate Henry
4 Holmes Mrs
5 Cowen Albert
6 Mayland Oscar Charles
Gant DB (dining rooms)
*here is Alexandra Dock*
### South side
1 Hammond Harry
2 Bunton Frederick A (coal merchant)
Minister Robert
Stanton JT & Co. Ltd. (timber merchants)
**Dock Hotel** (Emma Elvina Kendle)
*here is North Street*

The St James Theatre in St James' Place burnt down in 1937. Firemen damp down the rubble. This Theatre was never rebuilt. Vancouver House now stands on the site.

**ST. ANN'S MANSIONS**
*See St. Ann's Street*

**ST. ANN'S STREET**
*From Chapel Street to 7 St. Ann's Fort*
North side

Davis Mrs H (Listergate)
St. Nicholas' Church
     *here is Chapel Yard*
Humphrey Frederick S  (ship chandler)

**Hanover Yard***
Petts Arthur
Dexter Mrs

**St. Ann's Mansions**
1  Fisher Ernest
2  George William Robert
3  Scott Fred
4  Richardson Frederick Arthur
5  Chapman Mrs

6  Glyde Mrs

———

5  Seaman Martin Frederick (hairdresser)
4  Baxter Bert  (boot repairer)
3  Chase Mrs
2  Smith Charles  (dairyman)
1  **Naval Reserve PH   (Frederick William Franklin)**
     *here is North Street*
South side
     *here is St. Nicholas Street*
20 Bristow & Copley Ltd. (timber
    merchants)
St. Nicholas' Mission Hall
Sadler William R   JP (St Ann's House)
Robinson CR (St Ann's House)
Kerner-Greenwood & Co. Ltd.
(cement waterproofers)
Thatcher Ivan J (vice-consul for Belgium)
(North Hirne)
Flanders Harry

## ST. ANN'S STREET (continued)

Hornigold Frederick T
4 & 6 Bowers Walter R  (baker)
*here is Churchman's Yard*
Howard William Arthur  (greengrocer)
Burrell JF  (grocer & post office))

## ST. JAMES' PLACE
*From County Court Road*
### North side

1  Holmes Samuel John
2  Doughty Ernest P  (shopkeeper)
3  Skipper Arthur
Spotted Cow PH  (Robert Simmons)
5  Wrightson John
6  Waterhouse Mrs Catherine (certified midwife)
*here is South Street*
7  Walpole John Thomas
8  Cooper Bert
9  Bouch Wilfred
10 Reeve Charles
*here is Wood Street*
St. James' Council School (infants)
### South side
St. James' Theatre (William Adams, manager)
Hopkins H, MInstM & CE, AMIStructE,
MRSanI, (assistant county surveyor to the
Norfolk County Council (St. James' House)
Norfolk County Council (Western Highways)
Weights & Measures (St James House)

## ST. JAMES' ROAD
*From 65 St. James' Street*
*to 72 Blackfriars Street*
### South side
*here is South Clough Lane*
3  Bales Edward   (shopkeeper)
4  Harrod Miss E
5  Green Miss Louisa M  (confectioner)
6  Walden Walter
7  Flanders Arthur  (fishmonger)
8  Orviss Robert

9  Fayers Henry
10  Metcalf Ernest
11  Kenzie Walter
12  Manning George W (carpenter)
13  Riches George Edward
14  Day Alfred
St. James' Almshouses
Domestic Training Centre
16  Cross William George
17  Rumbelow John
Smith's Buildings (almshouses)
18  Reynolds Miss
Johnson W H & Sons Ltd.  (garage)
19  Bowes Fred
20  Watts & Rowe  (general printers)
21  Johnson W H & Sons Ltd.
(motor engineers) (showroom)
*here are Blackfriars Street & Railway Road*
### North side
*here is St. James' Park*

## ST. JAMES' STREET
*From Saturday Market Place*
*to London Road*
### South side
*here is Church Street*
Piper Arthur  (hairdresser)
2 Ivy Madame  (milliner)
4 Errington Robert George  (tailor)
6 Westwood Misses  (confectioners)
8 Carter & Jarvis  (fruiterers)
10 Stokeley Robert  (tobacconist)
12 Norfolk Dairies (Alcock & Appleby)
14 **Three Pigeons PH  (Joseph W Evans)**
16 Miller Ronald  (newsagent)
16 Greeves James William
*here is Brown's Yard*
18 Johnson  WH & Sons Ltd. (motor
engineers)
20 King's Lynn Gas Co

## ST. JAMES' STREET (continued)

22 Hurn Herbert William (dairyman)
24 & 26 Johnson WH & Sons Ltd.
(motor engineers) (offices)
28 Bennell FW & Son (confectioner)
30 Sawyer AG (butcher)
32 Powell Herbert R (boot maker)
36 Johnson WH & Sons Ltd.
 (motor engineers)
*here is Tower Place*
Theatre Royal (Ernest R Adams, manager)
*here are Tower Gardens & London Road*

### North side

1 **White Hart PH (Joseph B Hendry)**
3 Bowman Henry S
5 County Electrical Services Ltd.
(electrical engineers)
King's Lynn YMCA (HW Riley, hon sec)
9 & 11 Flatte Miss Mabelle (draper)
King's Lynn & West Norfolk Conservative
Club Co. Ltd. (FGW Hayes, sec)
(St James House)
St. James' Club (J Cross, sec)
King's Lynn Men's Conservative Club (Sidney
Pedder, sec)
15 Jefferies William Henry (watch maker)
15 Jefferies Leonard (auctioneer)
17 Hall Mrs Freda (milliner)
19 Johnson WH & Sons Ltd (motor depot)
21 Sayer Alfred (tobacconist)
23 Roy & Son (bill posters)
25 Ward John Samuel (florist)
27 Reed William (hairdresser)
29 Proctor WH & Co (coal merchants)
29a Bears Corn Stores (corn merchants)
*here is Tower Street*
35 Crawford Mrs MA (confectioner)
Building Material Co. (King's Lynn) Ltd.
*here is Tower Court*
39 Gift Shop (The) (EI Oxby)
41 Johnson Frank M (jeweller)
43 Gooding Stanley (hairdresser)

45 Dobson Mrs Norah (confectioner)
47 & 49 Walton Bros. (King's Lynn
& Hunstanton) Ltd. (drapers)
51 Spaxman Cyril (fruiterer)
53 Audrey Madame (ladies hairdresser)
53 Dobson Albert (tobacconist)
55 Eileen Madame (costumier)
*here is Regent Place*
57 Baldero Frederick (confectioner)
57 Harris Mrs AM (corsetiere)
59 Dow Alfred Edward (chemist)
61 Johnson Bert, Johnson WH & Sons Ltd.
(garage)
63 Pridgeon Miss E
65 Stain Thomas Henry
*here are St. James' & London Roads*

### ST. JOHN'S COTTAGES
*From 5 John Street*

1 Ellis Miss
2 Smith Frederick William
3 Brighton Mrs E

### ST. JOHN'S TERRACE
*From Blackfriars Street to Blackfriars Road*

1 Elvin John Robert
2 Curson Reginald
2 Greene Arthur MA, MDDub (ophthalmic
surgeon)
3 Newton Misses
4 Browne Robert Thomas
5 Curtis George James
6 Warren Mrs WQ
7 Livermore Herbert John
8 Matthews Miss Jane (dressmaker)
9 —
10 Miles Frederick John JP
11 Carman Phillip Henry
12 Collison Miss
13 —
Letzer Sydney Henry (Belgrave House)

A lone car (Austin 7?) is parked on the Saturday Market Place in about 1936

### West side
Lincoln Alfred  (Ermington House)
Garland & Flexman  (ship brokers)
Palmer Alfred. vice-consul for
Denmark, Norway, Sweden & Spain
8 Beaty George  (blacksmith)
9 Ashton Edward
9 Stokes Alfred  (hairdresser)
Tilson  Herbert T  LRIBA (architect)
*here is St. Ann's Street*

### ST. MARGARET'S PLACE
*From 33 Queen Street to Nelson Street*
### West side
Bowker A & J  (maltsters)
Parker  Spencer T, MB, ChB, LRCPLond, FRCS
Eng, (ophthalmic surgeon)
Floyd William H
Knowles Rev. Maurice Hinton MA
(vicar of St. Margaret's & rural dean of Lynn (St.
Margaret's vicarage)
Floyd Frank R  (corn merchant)  (St.
Margaret's House)
### East side
St. Margaret's Church

### ST MICHAEL'S TERRACE
*See Saddlebow Road*

### ST. NICHOLAS STREET
*From 63 Chapel Street to Tuesday Market Place*
### East side
White William  (builder)
St. Nicholas Drill Hall
*here is Seed's Yard*
**Duke of Connaught PH  (William James Ely)**
St. Nicholas Chambers
*here is Bennett's Yard*
20 Leman Miss
19 Parsell William Francis
*here are Sacker's Buildings*
Moy Miss Elizabeth  (shopkeeper)

### SALTER'S ROAD♦
*From 29 Gaywood Road*
### East side
1  Burrows Albert James
2  Fayers Sidney
3  Fisher Herbert
4  Tooley Albert
5  Bunting Alfred
*here is Fermoy Avenue*
6  Krill Albert Victor
7  Thompson George
8  Holt Albert W
9  Brooks John
10 Bracher Frederick Charles
Cowell Alfred. (The Gatehouse)
Brooker Frederick (Mill House)
Thwite James (Mill Cottage)
*here is Loke Road extension*
### West side
13  Isbill Reginald
14  Barnes Sidney
15  Buttle Arthur
16  Davies Mrs
17  Sands Robert
18  Crisp Mrs
19  Johnson Donald
20  Gordon William
White's Nurseries  (John White, nurseryman)

## SATURDAY MARKET PLACE
*From St. James' Street to*
*St. Margaret's Place*

1 Maison St. Margaret (millinery - Williamson Mrs)

Hallack & Bond (Wholesale) (wholesale grocers) (warehouse)

Brooker Frederick

2 Lincolns (antique dealers)

3 Crisp Wallace William MPS (chemist)

4 Medlock Herbert R (confectioner)

6 **Duke of Fife PH (John Robert Dawson)**

6 Prior Edward H (butcher)

7 Smith Bros (hardware dealers)
*here is High Street*

9 Betts Mrs Jessie S wardrobe (dealer)

Curson Charles William (Oregon)

Cook Mrs AE (apartments)

Young Henry William

Borough Police Station (Henry W Young) (chief constable, inspector of weights & measures, petroleum & explosives & hackney carriages)

Guildhall (Johnson William Woolstencroft, town clerk)

JC Matthew AMICE (borough surveyor & engineer to the King's Lvnn Water Works), John William Shaw (sanitary inspector) & L Hall (hall keeper)

## SEDGEFORD LANE
*From 26 High Street to*
*Tower Street/Baxter's Plain*
### North side

41 Chilvers George

40 Smith William
  Bunn C Edwin

39 Hornigold Horace Benjamin

38 Simpson Robert

37 Gray Charles

35 Bunn Jack

33 King Oliver S

32 Starling Frederick

31 Park Mrs Ethel M (shopkeeper)

30 Hunter Mrs D

29 Sharman John Thomas (shopkeeper)

28 **Foresters Arms - Beerhouse (Bertie Whitmore)**

27 Rose Harry

27a Malt Alfred

27b Freeur Arthur
### South side
Copeman Fred (electrical contractor)
*here is Cross Lane*

16 Lusher Henry George

15 Futter Mrs

14 Burrows James

13 SEnter Fred
*here is Mills Yard*

12 Blyth George David

11 Thomas James

10 Moore Henry

9 Hood Albert

8 Griffin Mrs

6 Miller Mrs

## SEED'S YARD
*From St. Nicholas Street*

1 —

2 Setchell John

3 —

4 —

## SELBY PLACE
*From 7 Valinger's Place*
### South side

1 Williamson Jack

2 Moule Reginald Percy

3 Tilson Harold

4 Auker William Ambrose

127

## SIDNEY STREET

*From 68 Vancouver Avenue*

*to Chase Avenue*

### South side

2  Howard Mrs E
4  Stephenson Arthur Percy
6  D'Oyly Watkins Robert
8  Rayner Ernest Samuel
10 Longman Harold Benjamin
12 Verry Mrs
14 Trim Arthur
16 Wilson Mrs Mary

*here is Somerville Road*

18 Brunning Rev. Ernest R  BA  (curate of All Saints
20 East Noel
22 Beaver Austin MB
24 Ashling Edward Howard
26 Scott Thomas
28 Fletcher Joshua
30 Sketcher Ernest
32 Girling Wm. John
32 Girling Miss Gladys  (hosier)
34 Thomas Wallace Adams
36 Hancock Percy
38 Hall Henry
40 Bacon Harry
42 Lambert Cecil H
44 Munns Harold Edward
46 Bremner Rev. Eustace W  Congregational)
48 Smith Harry Charles
50 Eglinton Edgar V
52 Pooley John
54 Shinn Walter
56 Bass Thomas James
58 Chapman Reginald T

60 Lyons Edward
62 Allen Frederick. Chas
64 Emmerson Leonard
68 Rust Mrs E
70 Wilson Frank
72 Senior Charles H
74 Broad Thomas William
76 Mendham Rodwell
78 Batch Isaac
80 Sparrow Frederick William
82 Bray Albert Edward
84 Butt Christopher
86 Fachney Alexander John

### North side

3  Haverson James A
5  Aldridge William Robert
7  Docking Mrs
9  Slator Frederick William
11 Cain Miss H
13 Anderson George James
15 Wisker Mrs
17 Mitcham Arthur
19 Bissell William John
21 Horn Sidney
23 Fawcett Guy S
25 Denman William Marter
27 Dixon Joseph
29 Greeves William Henry
31 Coleman Leonard John
33 Smurden William
35 Alexander George Robert
37 Davison Oliver Lionel
39 Gooding George
41 Harris John
43 Curtis Mrs
45 Easter Leonard George
47 Hares Ernest James
49 —
51 Le Grice Douglas Meadows
53 English Percy
55 Jervis Walter

## SILFIELD TERRACE
*From 78 Tennyson Road*
### North side
10 —
9 Purchase John
8 Rolfe Ernest
7 Taylor Ryley W
6 Hignell Alfred Charles
5 Hill George Robert
4 Stevens Horace Francis
3 Fysh Herbert William
2 Kisby Horace
1 Walker William L

## SIMPSON'S YARD*
*From 15 All Saints Street*
2 Brown Ernest
3 Hudson Matthew
4 Birch Sidney

## SIR LEWIS STREET
*From 7 Loke Road*
### East side
1 Smith Bertie   (shopkeeper)
3 Hornigold Frederick
5 Nichols Mrs
9 Walker Robert John
11 Williamson John
13 Roper William
15 Machin T
17 Edmunds George
Chase Charles   (shrimp merchant)
Marion Almshouses
19 Ridout Harry M   (baker)
21 Allen Robert
23 Wright John
25 Wright Charles William
27 Hammond John Thomas
29 Smith Thomas

The South Gates in 1937. The Ford garage at this time is owned by John Davy.

## SIR LEWIS STREET (continued)

31 Hammond Robert
33 Dowdy Herbert
35 Goldsmith Mrs
37 Marsters John
39 Veal George
41 Bone John
59 Chase Matthew  senior
61 Chase Charles William
63 Chase Matthew
65 Bunting Robert
67 Gay James
69 Tungate Robert
71 Oakes Thomas Edward
73 Reynolds Robert Charles
75 Snelling William
77 Howard Thomas
79 Savage William
81 Whiley Alfred James
83 Potter Mrs

85 Bunting Sidney
87 Chase Mrs
89 —

### West side

2  Saunders Leonard
2  Saunders Leonard  junior  (insurance agent)
4  Carter Thomas James  (shopkeeper)
6  Hall Albert Edward
8  Backham Mrs
10  Pratt Mrs
12 Collison Herbert
14 Fenton John
16 Dunbabin Frederick
18 Bowers William
20 Gay Ernest
22 Green Mrs
24 Daniels William
26 Fysh John Robert
28 Marshall Arthur George
30 Spooner BG
32 Anderson William
34 Bray Henry
36 Maxwell Arthur George
38 Minister Robert
40 Fysh John W
42 Bone James
44 Watts Charles
46 Stafford Alfred
48 Southgate Jack
50 Groom Joseph
52 Williamson Walter E  (fish shop)
*here is Walker Street*
54 Frost Edward
56 Marshall Sidney
58 Flanders Harry
60 Barnard Mrs
62 Delahoy Matthew
64 Petts Thomas H
66 Chase George
68 Balls Frederick
70 Anderson William G
72 Lake Horace

The steam tug Conservator is moored at the South Quay in 1937. In the background is the Boal Quay.

**SIR LEWIS STREET (continued)**

74 Pickett Sidney
76 Moy William
78 Curston Thomas A
80 Baker Alfred Frederick
82 Pickett Percy William

**SMITH AVENUE**
*From 13 Raby Avenue to*
*1 Townsend Terrace*
North side

1 Chapman Herbert
3 Knights Robert
5 Pegg Albert
7 Marshall Benjamin John
9 Senter Albert George

11 Dennis George Gilbert
13 Rudd Frederick
15 Bridges Frederick
17 Townley John
19 Buntin Ernest
21 Howard William
23 Nurse William A
25 Dunn Leslie H
27 Goodson Thomas
29 Delaney Frank
31 Dexter William
33 Groom George
35 Crome Christopher
*here is Townsend Terrace*
South side
2 Coe P Manning

## SMITH AVENUE (continued)

4 Bailey Jacob
6 Chase Sidney Edward
8 Webster William James
10 English Sidney R
12 Chase Robert
14 Simpson William E
16 Armes George T
18 Neave Alfred
20 Gardener John
22 Smith George Edward
24 Griffin Norris
26 Shread J William R
28 Ward Benjamin Harry
*here is Townsend Terrace*

## SMITH'S CHAMBERS
*See High Street*

## SOFTLY'S YARD
*From 7 Broad Street*
2 Pottele Walter. Henry
3 Benjamin William

## SOMERVILLE ROAD
*From 16 Sidney Street to 1 Argyle Street*
1 Hewitt Frederick Charles William
2 Chapman William Sidney
3 Garrod Charles Henry
4 Futter Robert

## SOUTH GATES
*From Wisbech Road to 60a London Road*
### West side
5a **Prince of Wales Hotel   (John D Laws)**
5 Laws John David   (boot repairer)
4 Proctor Percy
4 Dye Robert William (builder)
2 Davy John F   (Ford dealer)
1 Poctor William Henry & Co.  (coal merchants)

## SOUTH QUAY
*From King Staith Lane to Boal Quay*
Wittred Frederick Henry   (coal merchant)
Skerry Ernest Edward  (coal merchant)
Scott & Son   (house furnishers)
Thrower & Co.  (mineral water manufacturers)
*here is College Lane*
Green Richard  (plasterer - warehouse)
Williamson Mrs
**Mariners' Arms PH   (Frederick L Pitt)**
Gregorys & Hampson,  (corn merchants)

## SOUTH STREET
*From 6 St. James' Place to 21 Wood Street*
### North side
1 Baker Wilfred
3 Godfrey Mrs GN
5 Richards Leslie
7 Dawson George
9 Triscott Alfred Herbert
11 Pearman William Thomas
13 Kirby George
15 Bailey Mrs
17 Parfrement Alfred
19 Osborne Mrs
21 Sporne William  (grocer)
23 Lane Mrs
25 Joplin Eric
27 East Thomas
29 Baker Mrs
31 Kirby Mrs M
33 Hewitt Donald Digby
35 Kirby William Charles
37 Browne Ernest William
39 Hill George John
41 Hidd Mrs
43 Dennis George P
45 Miller Elijah
47 McCusker John
49 Culey Stanley Frank
51 Rackham George

## SOUTH STREET (continued)

53  Lake George Walter

### South side

62 Thody George Henry
60 Barnard William
58 Woomes James William
56 Gamble Robert
54 Chapman Miss
52 Hall Bert
50 Copeman Frederick
48 Beaney Walter
46 Whiley J
44 Fenton Alfred
42 Bannister Edward William
40 Gribble Alfred
38 Grange Frederick
36 Bocking George D
34 Nooth Charles John
32 Taylor Mark
30 King Mrs
28 Hawes Ernest
26 Bray Mrs E
24 Harding Samuel
22 Anderson Robert J
20 Mears Mrs
18 Mindham Mrs
16 Kerrison Robert Henry
14 Anderson George
12 Jopling Sidney Arthur
10 Hubbard Thomas
8  Wright Charles E
6  Catton William Horace   (baker)

## SOUTH CLOUGH LANE

*From 3 St. James' Road to 3 Tower Street*

### South side

1  Chase Matthew
2  Pearman Ernest C
3  Hider Mrs EE   (general shop)
          *here is Bentinck Street*
5  Capps Thomas   (boot repairer)
7  Towler George

50 South Clough Lane in 1934. Reputed to be the smallest house in Lynn. Squeezed on to a plot between two houses in about 1830 it had a front room only 7 feet wide, 10 feet deep and 6ft 6ins high. There was a slightly larger room at the back, a small scullery and a very small yard.

9  Mattin George
11 Brown Mrs M   (draper)
13 Brundle Walter   (fried fish shop)
          *here is Melbourne Street*
15 **Rose & Thistle PH   (George Gordon Baker)**
19 Booty Albert R
          *here is Regent  Street*

## SOUTH CLOUGH LANE (continued)

21 Lane Mrs Jemima   (shopkeeper)
23 Ball Robert Stanley
25 Arnop Frederick
27 Horsley David R
29 Bostman Albion H
31 Brown Mrs M  (confectioner)
33 Barker Herbert Walter
35 Mercer John William
35a Tungay Mrs E
37a Bennett Mrs F
37 Bird Miss S
39 Dye Edward
41 Arnop Mrs GE  (general shop)
*here is Whincop Street*
43 Atkins Robert  (wardrobe dealer)
45 Payne Edward
*here is Trundles Yard*
47 Gibson William
Berry John (Elm House)

### North side

2  Greeves Frederick
4  Taylor Herbert Thomas
6  Bullock George William
8  Setchell Alfred Albert
10 Gamble William
*here is Blackfriars Passage*
18 Heil Frederick
20 Lord Harry
22 Heil Albert James
24 Shaw Harold Cooper  (dairyman)
26 Howard Edward Ernest
30 Robinson Charles
32 Rowe Mrs F
36 Long Thomas William
40 Smith Frederick  (tinsmith)
42 Pottle George
44 Jubey Mrs
46 Bullock Ernest
48 —
50 Meggitt Thomas William
52 Meggitt Edward Percy

56 Simpson William

## SOUTH EVERARD STREET
*From 35 Valingers Road to*
*79 London Road*
### North-east side

1  Herrell Mrs
2  Hassall James
3  Smith Leonard
4  Southgate Robert
*here is North Everard Street*
5  Stokes Mrs E
6  Wilcox Mrs
7  Anderson Arthur
8  Barrett J James
9  Catton William John
10 Cocks Arthur Edward
11 Proctor Charles William Atkins
12 Garrod Frederick
13 Walker Miss
14 Abbott Robert Charles
15 Monument Philip James
16 Sillett Ernest
17 Bray Edwin
18 Wright Sydney Walter
19 Hall Mrs ME
20 Cozens Francis
21 Clarke William Edward
22 Moore Mrs
23 Sharman William Steven
24 Curtis George Henry
*here is John Street*
### South-west side

25 Piper Arthur Albert
26 Baldwin James
27 Drew Mrs
28 Faulkner Mrs
29 **Stone Masons' Arms PH (Herb. Jarvis)**
30 Laws Mrs ME   (shopkeeper)
31 Lewis Mrs
32 Holmes Harvey James
33 Barnaby Mrs

## SOUTH EVERARD STREET (continued)

34 Williamson William
35 Lewis Henry Denton
36 Petts Frederick Henry
37 Pryke William P
38 Register John Eustace
39 Peacock George
40 Townsend Albert
41 Skerry Frederick Charles
42 Proctor Horace Edward
43 Scott George Walter
44 Goat Stanley
Ives Thomas & Sons   (builders)
45 Thurston George Edwin
46 Drew Mrs
All Saints' (C of E) School (boys, girls & infants)
47 Fordham Thomas   (baker)
48a Ryan Mrs
48b Sharpin Thomas
48 Brown Reginald
49 Seals Robert Walter
50 Regester Albert Edward
52 Joplin Alfred
53 Pack Clarence Victor
54 Pack Charles Reginald
55 Barnes William

## SOUTH LYNN ENVIRONS
*From Saddlebow*

Saunders William Ernest
Moses Horace   (farmer)
Pitcher Frank   (nurseryman) (Seeche Abbey)
Towler George   (farmer) (Seeche Farm)
Towler George Walter  junior   (farmer) (Seeche House)

## LNER Railway  (siding)

Chenery Frank   (Gate House)
Kidman William
Addison John
Howes William

Johnson James Robert
Allen & Deck  (farmers)  (Seeche Manor Farm)
Allen Claude (Seeche Manor farm)

## SOUTH LYNN PLAIN
*From 1 Valingers Road to 1 Friars Street*
### South-west side
**Crossways PH   (Nellie Williamson)**
Lavender William L (Valentine House)
*here is Friars Place*
Pointer Augustus P   (motor garage)
Lee George   (fried fish dealer)
*here is Friars Street*
4 Baker Miss M   (fried fish dealer)
*here are All Saints Street & Church Lane*
6 **Anchor Inn   (Reginald Brown, then Frederick Walker from July 1933)**
8 Drewery Alfred
8 Carman Leonard   (insurance agent)
8 Drewery AWL   junior
9 Bennett Henry   (tailor)
9 Taylor Mrs
Valingers Almshouses

## SOUTHFIELD TERRACE
*See Saddlebow Road*

## SOUTHGATE COURT
*From 2 Southgate Street*
4 Pratt Mrs SA
5 Suter Mrs
6 Potter William Thomas
7 Suter George
8 Castle Richard
11 Stebbings John
12 Curson James
14 Funnell Robert
15 Shepheard Mrs E

## SOUTHGATE STREET
*From 60 London Road to 83 Friars Street*
### North-east side
1 Green Edward
2 Bowley Mrs
    *here is Southgate Court*
3 Watts Arthur
7 **Chequers PH  (Walter Charles Curtis)**
    *here is Horsley's Court*
8 Blatch James William
9 Raper James
10 Purt Mrs
11 Branford Mrs
12 Blyth Alfred
12 Smith Frederick C
13 Proctor William Leslie
14 Skerry Samuel C
15 Failes Mrs
16 Shafto Edwin
### South-west side
*here is Cromwell Terrace*
Woodend John C  (Bay House)
Bone Robert  (builder)  (workshop)
18 Link John Samuel
19 Proctor Sydney
20 Groom Thomas William
21 Jolley Frederick  (firewood dealer)
22 Thurston Victor
Slator John William & Sons (agricultural engineers)

## SPENCERS SQUARE
*From 19 Checker Street*
1 Nicholls Robert William   junior
2 Day Mrs A
3 Fiddiman Reginald
4 Nobbs Herbert George
5 Greenacre William
6 Edwards Thomas
7 Day William
8 Nicholls Mrs
   Lambert Thomas

## STAGG ROW
*From Front Row, Highgate*
1 Frost Harry V
2 Cooper Arthur Elliott
3 Thrower Albert
4 Laws Mrs
5 Fountain Mrs
6 Collison Mrs
7 Maxwell Mrs
8 Benefer Mrs
9 Footer Henry

## STANLEY STREET
*From 57 Railway Road to 10 Bedford Street*
### East side
1 Empson Miss
   Smalls Hubert    (basket maker) (workshop)
2 Barrett George Edward
3 Bell Albert George
4 Curtis Mrs
5 Rayner Edward J
6 Harrod Charles
7 Stanforth Harry
8 Hitchcock Percy William
9 Hall Harry
10 Elsegood Walter Thomas
11 Westmoreland James Frederick
12 Palmer Mrs
13 Winter Ernest
14 Johnson Miss AM
15 Johnson Mrs E
16 Muffett Jack
17 Watson John
18 Ransom Albert George
### West side
23 Haines Arthur Edward
22 Peck Miss
21 Hendry Harry B
20 Linford Stanley
Avery W & T Ltd.  (scale makers)
19 Franklin David

## STONEGATE STREET

*Continuation of Greyfriars Road &*
*Millfleet Terrace to Church Street*

### North side

*here is Tower Place*

1 Gibson Mrs Ellen (bill poster)
   Bolton RH & Co. Ltd. (printers)
2 King's Lynn Liberal Club (PF Green,
   secretary & treasurer)
3 Ryan Ernest
4 Harrison George

*here is Andrew's Yard*

5 Parlett Charles John
   Gorbould Bros. (motor engineers)
6 Gorbould Frederick Birkett
7 Shallow George S
8 Neal Miss Daisy (music teacher)

*here is Crisp's Yard*

9 Hulme Oscar Charles
10 Bocking Stanley Charles (newsagent)

### South side

Morgan's Brewery Co. Ltd. (Lady Bridge
brewery)

## SUGAR'S ALMSHOUSES

*See Goodwin's Road*

## SURREY SQUARE

*From Baptist Chapel Yard*

1 Anderson Thomas A
2 Isabel Charles
3 Ely John
4 Millington George

## SURREY STREET

*From 11 Chapel Street to 64 High Street*

### East side

1 Howard Henry
2 Johnson George
   Everitt William James (rag merchant)
4 —
5 Gazley John
   Skinner John & Sons (rag merchants)
   Setchell RH (fruit merchant)

### West side

Everitt William James (rag merchant) (office)
Skinner John & Sons (rag merchants) (office)
Setchell RH (wholesale fruit merchant) (office)

A Great Central class D9 passes over Tennyson Avenue with a Dereham train in 1936.

### SWISS TERRACE

*From 99 Tennyson Avenue*

1 Fenn Sidney
2 Myhill Bert
3 Nelson Thomas
4 Foreman James
5 Rippengill John
6 Salmon Thomas

### SYDNEY TERRACE

*From 14 Cornwall Terrace, Saddlebow Road*

1 Palmer Walter
2 Breeze Reginald
3 Leake Harold Thompson
4 Burton Isaac

5 Petts Henry
6 Leman Henry John
7 Buck Mrs
8 Tokelove John
9 Hewitt George
10 Robinson John William

### TENNYSON AVENUE

*From 112 Gaywood Road*
*to Tennyson Road*

East side

Roberts Thomas Edward (Woodford)
Ware Sidney (Salford House)
1 Scott William
2 Frost William

August Bank Holiday in 1935 and the traffic heading through town from the A10, A17 and A47 to the coast queues on Tennyson Road. There was talk of a subway under the railway crossing or a bridge over the crossing at this time but like many schemes it was only talk.

## TENNYSON AVENUE (continued)

3  Hayhow Geoffrey
4  Hill Miss EM
5  Love John H
6  Ball Charles
7  —
8  Sheldon Henry
8  King's Lynn School of Music (Miss E Sheldon LRAM, MRST, & Miss NL Sheldon ATCL, MRST) (principals)
8  Sheldon Miss Eveline R, ABWS  (teacher of drawing)
9  Walling AE Russell
10  Woolstencroft JW
11  Goddard George
12  Giles Theodore W
13  Kirkland Frederick G
14  Frost Horace  (grocer & post office)
15  Cross Jabez
16  Savage John
17  Chatten Frank
18  Hilling Frank
19  Brown James
20  Spurge Albert Sidney
21  Bray Ernest
22  Saward William S
23  Howard Alfred
24  Walker Robert
25  Howard Stanley Charles
26  Beeston James
27  Bromhead Thomas J
28  Elliott Percy Cristall
29  Grave Walter
30  Hitchcock Miss
31  Whitehouse Bertram
32  Smith Edward
33  Spinks George William
34  Wildbur Wilfrid Robert
35  Bell Mrs
36  Bocking Mrs
37  Bearman Mrs S  (dressmaker)
38  Taylor James William
39  Goff Herbert John
40  Baxter William Henry
41  Tweedy   (collector of cattle market tolls)
42  Pooley Charles Henry
43  Cann Walter George
44  Harrison Frederick G
45  Hodson Mrs MA
46  Hall Miss EL
47  Harbage Mrs J
48  Moore Leonard Richard
49  Harbage Mrs J
50  Wilson Miss
51  Gibbons James Charles
52  Patrick Mrs
53  Knowles Arthur
54  Bocking Reginald
55  Stevens Samuel
56  Pooley Harry
57  Anderson Ernest William
58  Bly Ernest
69  Watts Mrs
60  Thorpe Henry Frank
61  Palmer John
62  Gunston Albert John
63  Southgate Reginald
64  Matthews William James
65  Anderson Mrs
    *here is Tennyson Avenue railway crossing*

### West side

Morton Mrs ES (Lynncroft)
Fachney George (Denehurst)
Alderton Ronald T (Claymore)
Rose James George (Sunrise)
Taylor John Henry (Camdene)
Mortimer Sydney A (Granta)
Harper Alfred (Escar)
Piper Mrs EM (Elna)
    *here is Milton Avenue*
Eyles Cecil (Lynwood)
Freeman Arthur William (Maiscot)
Pitts Tom (Tadcaster)

| TENNYSON AVENUE (continued) | | *here is Swiss Terrace* |
|---|---|---|

**TENNYSON AVENUE (continued)**

Sedgley Mrs J W  (Sedgholm)
Milton Service Garage (J D Watson, proprietor)
111 Trew George Baker
110 Sneath Frank Newton
109 Scholey Claude Vickers
108 Jones Mrs CJ
107 Booty John Frederick
106 Harrison Hubert Godfrey
105  Skeels Sidney
104 Dunbabin Mrs
103 Lawson Harry
102 Barnard Mrs
101 Martin William
100 Francis Henry
99 Giles John Edward
Watson Mrs H (Swiss Cottage)

*here is Swiss Terrace*

98 Lilley Mrs
97 Peake Mrs
96 Lincon James
95 Street George

**TENNYSON ROAD**
*From Tennyson Avenue to Exton's Road*
South-east side

66  Mitchell Percy Lewis
67  Grange Charles
68  Falk Albert
69  Free Frederick
70  Levey Edward
71  Smith Mrs
72  Watts Thomas
73  Seaman George Edward
74  Barnard Edwin
75  Procter Robert
76  Mace Albert Edward
77  Palmer Arthur
78  Skate Mrs
*here is Silfield Terrace*
79  Taylor Miss MA
80  Meadows Miss
81  Fuller Walter
82  Hammond Mrs
83  Carr Ernest James
84  Count Sidney
85  Wilson Mrs
*here are Mount Street & Park Avenue*
86  Burton Thomas
86  Burton Mrs Ethel  MB, ChB
87  Green James
88  Hignell Frederick Henry
89  Whittingham WS
90  Furbank Mrs
91  Bunkall Mrs
92  Mitchell John B
93  Gilchrist Charles
Belton Mrs (Ongar House)
*here is Avenue Road*

## TENNYSON ROAD (continued)

Gillett John D (Avenue House)

Smith Robert A (Felixville)

Bowers Ely (Dane lodge)

Lubbock Mrs (Lynton)

Hook Edwin M (Glascoed)

Summerlin Frank Austin (Kinver Edge)

Lyon Misses (Clevelands)

Hitchcock Arthur (Tamworth House)

Winkley W Dinsdale (Ingleton)

Holman Lacey (Linthorpe)

### THE FRIARS
*See Friars (The)*

### THOMAS STREET
*From 7 Guanock Terrace*
#### South side

1  Dodman William
2  Laws George Samuel
3  Turtle William
4  Smith Frederick Thomas
   *here is Robert Street*
5  Benstead William George
6  Nurse Richard Frederick
7  Green Mrs Gertrude
8  Fakenbridge Richard
9  Smith Ambrose
10  Hooks Frederick
11  Watson Frederick James
12  Ellis James
13  Bushell Frederick
14  Newdick Mrs HE
15  Walker George Stephen
   *here is William Street*
#### North side
16a Pearman Arthur

#### Chase Cottages
1  Seaman Edward Henry
2  Leader Arthur
3  Harris Robert

Trues Yard in 1933.

*here is York Road*

16  Townsend Mrs H
17  Seaman James
18  Mitchley Robert

### THROWER'S YARD
*See Austin Street*

### TOWER COURT
*From 39 St James Street*

5  Grummett Mrs
4  Flood Mrs A
3  Hill Theobald
2  Hudson Mrs
1  Widdicombe Victor

## TOWER PLACE
*From St. James' Street to Stonegate Street*
### West side
Johnson W H & Sons Ltd. (motor works)
3 Green Richard (PF Green)
(fibrous plaster manufacturer)
Green Paine Franklin
Hales Thomas Alfred (Greyfriars House)
Bolton RH & Co Ltd (printers)
### East side
Turner Mrs MA
Jacobs George John (blacksmith)
Jack David Samson MRCVS (veterinary surgeon & veterinary inspector)

## TOWER STREET
*From St. James' Street to Baxter's Plain*
### South side
1 Edwards William Thomas (florist)
3 Blaxill Mrs FJ (milliner)
*here is South Clough Lane*
5 Berry Miss W (gowns)
7 Williams Frank (fruiterer)
9 Stone Miss Florence (tobacconist)
11 Daisley FH & Son (confectioners)
*here is Leaches Yard*
13 Loades Herbert (florist)
15 Docking William (fishmonger)
17 Bambridge's (fruiterers)
19 Goodson William (fishmonger)
19a Barber Harry EE
21 Barnaby Frederick (wallpaper merchant)
23 & 25 —
27 Bush Joseph (fishmonger)
29 Pratt John H
31 Medwell Miss Mabel (baby linen)
Wesleyan Methodist Church School Hall
33 Saunders William E
35 Bigg Albert Ernest (tailor)
37 Rust Mrs A
39 Gosling Edward (boot repairer)

Rummer PH (Frank Tyler)
### North side
Majestic Cinema (E R Adams, manager)
4 **Golden Ball PH (Ernest Ralph Adams)**
6 Bayes Charles (radio engineer)
8 Peckover Miss Agnes (tobacconist)
10 Starling Robert B (confectioner)
12 Hill Miss Alice (tobacconist)
14 Howard PW (butcher)
*here is Union Lane*
16 Verry R (sports outfitter)
18 Watsons' (picture frame makers)
*here are Bennett's Yard & Batterbee Court*
20 Batterbee & Co. (pork butchers)
22 Lancaster William A (butcher)
24 Brown Charles (confectioner)
26 —
28 Francis Joseph E (grocer)
Brooker Frederick (garage)
Wesleyan Methodist Church
30 Edwards Charles William
32 Wittred Frederick Henry (tobacconist)
34 Wittred Frederick Henry
36 Cresey Charles Robert (boot maker)
38 Spinks Alfred (confectioner)

## TOWNSEND TERRACE
*From 12 Smith Avenue to Salters Road*
1 Gough Frank
2 Skerritt Arthur
3 Howard Mrs
4 Reynolds Miss
5 Engledow John
6 Chase Charles
7 Guy James
8 Fiddy Horace Arthur

142

A busy Tuesday Market in 1937.

## TRUE'S YARD*
*From 11 North Street*

Lusher Percy R
1   Curson Harold King
2   Harper Joseph
3   Guy Stanley Herbert
4   Benefer Edward
5   Solly George
6   Goldsmith Edward George

## TUESDAY MARKET PLACE
*From 64 High Street*
### East side

1 & 2 Lloyds Bank Ltd. (Herbert Hilditch Adams, manager)
Neal's Restaurant
Clarkson H W & Son  (solicitors)
3 Middleton John Ellis, AMInstCE, FSI, LRIBA  (architect)
3 Inland Revenue Office (valuation department) C E Widdicombe, (district valuer)  (Bank Buildings)
Johnson Philip HH
Dow Horace Hamilton (registrar of births & deaths for the borough of King's Lynn & relieving officer, Norfolk County Council Guardians Committee, King's Lynn area) (Bank Buildings)
Rose John & Son  (saddlers, workshop)
National Provincial Bank Ltd., Hugh Greenwood (manager)
Harrison Hector, (caretaker)  (Bank Buildings)
3 Barclays Bank Ltd. (Tacon L Hart, manager)
**Duke's Head Hotel  (Kenneth Campbell McCallum)**
*here is Market Lane*
**Maid's Head Inn  (Edward James Setchell)**
King's Lynn Division of Norfolk Conservative & Unionist Association (AJL Ramm, sec & registration agent) (Unionist Chambers)
Jarvis & Morgan, (solicitors)
Uloth Alexander Wilmot MC, MA, MD, (physician & medical officer & public vaccinator Norfolk County Council Guardians Committee , Freebridge area).

## TUESDAY MARKET PLACE (continued)

Sadler & Lemmon (Herbert Gallienne Lemmon MA, LLM) (solicitors & notaries public)

Chamberlain GJH (vaccination officer King's Lynn Guardians Committee, area No 8)

**Victory Inn** (Cecil L Buckle)

*here is St. Nicholas Street*

### North side

Ebbs Charles (Northolme)

Pattrick & Thompsons Ltd. (timber merchants)

Debenham Capt. Charles Archer

Co-operative Insurance Society Ltd. (G Mallett, district manager) (Warton House)

Mallett George Charles (Warton House)

Roper Mrs

*here is Page Stair Lane*

### West side

Esses & Suffolk Equitable Insurance Society Ltd. (S. Seamer, local sec)

Culley & Co. (accountants)

Fen Finance Ltd. (regd. office)

Sommerfeld & Thomas Ltd. (road material merchants)

Gay & Wilson (sand merchants)

Hawkins Alan G & Co. (solicitors) & commissioners for oaths

Allflatt & Courtney (architects) (Hill House)

Scientific Poultry Breeder's Association Ltd

Hawkins Alan G, MA (solicitor & commissioner for oaths & clerk to the King's Lynn Conservancy Board (Hill House)

*here is Water Lane*

Corn Exchange (Arthur Deans, superintendent)

Barclays Bank Ltd. (T Blunt, manager)

Barclays Bank Ltd. (local head office)

*here is Ferry Street*

### South side

22 **Woolpack PH** (John Langley then James Caston from 06/03/1933)

## Bank Chambers

Hawkins Charles & The West Norfolk Farmers' Auction Co Ltd (auctioneers) (LG Hawkins FSI, Managing director)

Hawkins Charles & Sons (auctioneers & valuers, land & estate agents)

Gregory S & Son (auctioneers)

Jackson Donald Frederick (solicitor & commissioner for oaths & clerk to the Gaywood burial board & coroner for the King's Lynn district)

———

Ward Henry William (solicitor) (vice consul for the Netherlands & clerk to the borough justices)

Page Dudley S (solicitor & coroner for the borough)

23 "Gladhil" (The home-made cakeshop; morning coffee,teas etc.)

24 Norwich Union Fire Insurance Ltd. (GG Melton, resident inspector)

Cruso & Wilkin (house agents)

26 & 27 Jones & Dunn (gents' outfitters)

## UNION LANE

*From 14 Tower Street to 16 High Street*

### North side

Jackson Arthur Thomas (chimney sweep)

1 Wakefield Churchman

2 Curston Walter James

3 Warnes Frederick Robert

4 Taylor Arthur

5 Fisher Percy

6 Reddington Jack

7 Benefer Mrs

*here is Cross Lane*

12 Grass John

13 Brown Ernest

14 Capp Frederick

### South side

Union Lane Mission Hall

## UNION PLACE
*From Crooked Lane*
### West side
1 Benefer Mrs
2 Holland Harry
3 Manning John
4 Pearmain Robert
5 Baylis George
6 Culey John William
7 Edge Archibald
*here is Crome's Yard*
8 Rose Mrs C
9 Greenacre Walter
10 Woodhouse Sidney
### East side
1 Casey Misses
2 Snasdell James
3a Culey Joseph
4 Edge William   (fish salesman)
5 Bloye Oswald

## UNION STREET
*From Providence Street to*
*7 All Saints Street*
### South-east side
1 **Lynn Volunteer Stores  PH   (Henry Dexter Reed)**
2 Jones Arthur W
3 Starling Mrs
4 Wagg Horace
Sucker John  (coach painter)
Nurse William B  (cabinet maker)
5 Hardy William
6 Towler Harold
7 Castle Albert E
8 Turner Mrs
9 Robbins Mrs E
King's Lynn Society of Arts & Sciences
(C Webb, sec) (Welwick House)
Wykes George (Welwick House)
### North-west side
10  Hill Samuel Bertram

11 Gathercole Mrs E
12 Booty George Thomas  (pork butcher)
13 George Henry William
15 Bucke Mrs
16 Van Pelt Jan
17 Rainbow Sidney John
18 Shafto Albert Edward
20 Smith Jasper
21 Wright Mrs N   (shopkeeper)

## UNIONIST CHAMBERS
*See Tuesday Market Place*

## VALINGER'S PLACE
*From 3 Valinger's Road*
### West side
la Parnell Isaac
1 Britlin Thomas Robert
2 Darby George Richard
*here is Frederick Place*
3 Wilkerson Bertie Samuel
4 Marsters George Edward
5 Wilmore Arthur Charles
6 Earl Ambrose Edward
7 Fayers Alfred
*here is Selby Place*
### East side
8 Dexter Mrs
9 Reed Mrs
10 Benefer James
11 Dyble Walter Philip
12 Hendry George
13 Ward Percy Edwin
14 Allen George Thomas

## VALINGER'S ROAD
*From 11 South Lynn Plain*
*to 97 London Road*
### North side
1 Skerrey John Joseph (beer retailer)
2 Southerland Edwards Henry (butchers)
3 Chapman Miss K   (grocer)

## VALINGER'S ROAD (continued)

*here is Valinger's Place*

4 Hall Richard (plumber)
5 Graven Henry
6 Hill Thomas Benjamin
7 Garner Mrs
8 Lake Ernest Albert
9 Frost Mrs
10 Allan Robert
11 Suggett Alfred
12 Thompson A, MA
12 Thompson Miss
13 Dunmere Alfred Beresford MRCS Eng,
LRCP Lond (physician)
13 Dunmere Henzell Howard MC, FRCS Eng
(surgeon)
14 Dennick John I
15 Warner Edmund Herbert
16 Youngs Ernest
17 Veal Mrs H
18 Aspland François Harry
19a Chatterton & Co. (King's Lynn) Ltd.
(oil cake merchants)

### South side

Bell Leslie (electro plater)
18a Fuller Charles
19 Wing Charles Edward
20 Dodd Arthur
21 Webber Samuel George
22 Tweedy Sidney
22 Tweedy & Ward (builders)
23 & 24 King's Lynn & District Working
Men's Co-operative Society Ltd.
25 Adams Mrs
26 Moss John H
27 Suter Arthur
28 Holman Herbert Henry
29 Wilson Percy James
30 Fysh Alfred
31 Harrison Ernest (tailor)
32 Colquhoun Alex
33 Bouch Christopher Jacob

34 & 35 Mason Albert E (grocer)

## VANCOUVER AVENUE

*Form South Gates to Goodwin's Road*

### North side

Taylor Leo E (filling station)
Eastern Counties Omnibus Co. Ltd. (garage)
27 Drew Mrs
29 Whittaker Samuel Frederick
31 Rose Frederick
33 Ford John Edward
35 Rogers Mrs Emily
37 Brown Herbert
39 Wildbur Mrs AM
41 Harcourt Edgar Charles
43 Gathercole William
45 Brown Percy Sidney
47 Haigh Albert
47 Haigh Miss Ethel G (music teacher)
49 Hammond Robert Clarke
51 Watts Percy
53 Ransome Ronald Samuel
55 Hardy Robert Ashley
57 Hamaway John William
59 Goddard Walter
61 Goddard Bernard
63 Violen Alfred Edward
65 Bentley Henry Stephen
67 Hall Herbert
69 Randall Sydney George
71 Fyson Mrs

*here is York Road*

75 Ives Thomas
77 Wildbur William Thomas
79 Dewing Frederick James

### South side

14 Rivett William Robert
16 Aldridge Charles Arthur
18 Palmer Mrs
20 Sladden James Henry
22 Williamson John Frederick
24 Medlock George

Wanford Cottages in 1933.

## VANCOUVER AVENUE (continued)

26 Howlett Alfred Lee
28 Horsley Christmas G
30 Howlett James William (insurance agent)
32 Meadows George
34 Woodbine Richard
36 Barron Albert Edwin
38 Chaplin Frederick John
40 Scott Mrs
42 —
44 Housley James
46 Shinfield Alfred
50 Watson Robert Henry
52 Evetts Walter. Reginald
54 Read Mrs LJ
56 Waters Benjamin
58 Stratford John Daniel
60 Ebbs Wilfred
62 Aickman Mrs
64 Read Robert Ernest
66 Dawes George Theodore
58 Houlden Arthur
          *here is Sidney Street*
74 Ives Herbert
76 Clarke Bert

78 —
80 Crick Reginald. Albert
82 Horn John Charles
          *here is Chase Avenue*
86 Hodson Mrs

### VICARAGE LANE
*From 13 Providence Street to*
*Millfleet Terrace*
#### West side
1  Cox Mrs
2a Grange Mrs MA
3  Crow Frederick William
14 Baxter Ernest William
15 Coe Redvers GM
#### East side
2  Riches Frederick Henry
3  Sillis Robert William
          *here is Pump Yard*

The new drill hall in Wellesley Street in1936.

## VICTORIA BUILDINGS✦
*From 5 Lynn Road*

1  Burke Thomas
2  Allen Thomas John
3  Bunting Mrs
4  Pearman Ernest
5  Leader Frederick
   Hall Leonard  (Victoria Bungalow)
8  Patrick Robert
9  Simpson Robert

## VICTORIA STREET
*From 27 Windsor Road to Hospital Walk*
### East side
1  Child William Ernest
2  Cooper Ernest William
3  Lusher George
4  Allflatt Thomas
5  Leggett William John
6  Lowe Edmund
7  Bush Robert Leslie
8  Hawkins Christopher

9  Hood Robert Richard
10  Ling Mrs EM
11  Blockley Albert
12  Fox Michael Robert
13  Fleming Albert
### West side
14  Howard William
15  Melton Benjamin James
16  Clements Miss
17  Taylor Arthur
18  Thompson Wilfred Harry
19  Muncaster Henry Thomas
20  Manser John
21  Smith Alfred. Thomas
22  Hart Baden Mafeking
23  Stafford Alfred
24  Cozens Mrs
25  Moreley Herbert
26  Salt Mrs P
27  Hart Arthur Henry
28  Thurston Frederick James

Whincop Place 1933.

## WALKER STREET
*From Sir Lewis Street to Brick Yard*
### North side
*here are Cresswell & Burkitt Streets*
Smith Arthur E
Meek Albert William (insurance agent)
(Sunnyside)
Slatter Horace (Ivydale)
Thompson Frederick  (boot repairer)
### South side
*here are Cresswell & Burkitt Streets*
Smith Robert (Briar House)
1 Smith John
Bridges JS  (Mafeking House)

## WANFORD COTTAGES
*From 23 Wood Street*
1  Hall lrven Robert
2  Rowe Charles Frederick
3  Brundle Arthur Ernest
4  Shearman Mrs
5  Docking Leonard

## WATERLOO STREET
*From 33 Railway Road*
*to Blackfriars Road*
### West side
Ebling John B  (hairdresser)
Hilton J & Sons   (plasterers)
Hotel Cozens Garage
13 Lusher Fred
12 Hitch William
Jermyn  & Sons Ltd. (furniture repository)
England-Richards Fluid Free Cell Co.
The Eastern Radio Co.
### East side
1  Anderson Andrew
2  Rudd Miss
3  Shickle Frederick
4  Dickerson Ernest
6  Bailey Miss
6  Galloway Mrs

7  Brookes Miss
8  Chamberlain Mrs
9  Foreman Mrs
10  Ward Miss
11  Gathergood George William

## WATSON'S YARD
*From 13 Cross Lane*
Mindham Harry
Johnson Charles William

## WATSON'S YARD*
*From 19 North Street*
Twite William
Greenwood James
Norris James Duce
Ward Thomas

## WELLESLEY STREET
*From 48 Railway Road to Blackfriars Road*
### East side
Bassett Martin Augustus LDSRCS
(dental surgeon)
Edmonds Arthur Frank LDSRCS (dental
surgeon)
*here is Kirby Street*
Hallack & Bond (Wholesale) Ltd.
(wholesale grocery)  (Cranfield's Wharf)
### West side
1  Warman Mrs
2  Foster Mrs
3  Gibson Leonard John
4  Blyth Victor George
5  Williamson Victor George
Salvation Army Barracks
Whitmore John  (builder)
6  Langley Mrs
7  Allpress John
8  Westwood  Mrs F
9  Owen Thomas

## WELLINGTON COTTAGES
*See Hospital Walk*

## WELLINGTON STREET
*From 17 Windsor Road to Hospital Walk*
### West side
2  Hains Cecil Charles Edward
3  Thurlby Tom
4  Proctor Joseph Josiah
5  Blyth Leonard Denman
6  Juby John Silas
7  Fisher Miss
8  Taylor Alfred. Ernest
9  Dove Sydney F
10  Barratt Stanley
### East side
11  Sizeland Arthur Thomas
12  Eyles Charles
13  Wagg Percy William
14  Bussey James Stephen
15  Marsters Arthur William
16  Smith Thomas Twaits
17  Wagg Herbert Albert
18  Hildon John
19  —

## WHINCOP PLACE
*From South Clough Lane*
### North side
Pipe Louis Henry (Hope Cottage)
1  Wright Mrs L
2  Simpson John E
3  —
4  McKenzie James
5  Bocking William
6  Sayer James Freeman
7  Frost John
8  Raines Thomas Henry
### West side
Stebbings John Robert
Blyth Richard
Anderson Joseph

Ketteringham Sydney Arthur
Collison Bertram (Garden Cottage)
*here is Whincop Street*
### South side
10  Fisher Miss E
9  Chilvers Claude

## WHINCOP STREET
*From 10 Whincop Place to Regent Street*
### West side
1a  Wadlow Robert William
2a  Clark Charles
3a  Jarvis William George
4a  Murgett Arthur Henry
5a  Holmes Mrs
6  Wenn Alfred. John
Independent Club Ltd. (G Monument (sec)
### East side
1  Jackson John Richard
2  Bocking Albert W
3  Bruce George
4  Emerson George
5  Warner Miss
6a  Greeves John S
7  Collins Frank
8  Gribble Samuel
9  Crake Leonard Thomas
10  Pemment John Wallace
11  Bettinson Miss E

## WHITE LION COURT
*From 5 Norfolk Street*
Eldorado Ice Cream Co. Ltd
Barker  JH & Riches WE
(wholesale confectioners)
Peatling Thomas & Sons Ltd. wine
merchants (stores)

## WHITEFRIARS COTTAGES
*From 22 Friars Street*
### North-west side
1 Cooper Mrs
2 Manning Mrs A
3 Oakes Mrs Emily
4 Grummett Thomas

## WHITEFRIARS ROAD
*From Friars Street to The Friars*
### North side
1 Petrie Gerald D
2 Drew Harry
3 Teare Misses
4 Clamp Charles William
5 Reed James William
6 Seekings Albert Ernest
7 Parker Alfred
8 Rowe Miss
9 Curtis Charles Walter
10 Snasdell  John
11 Fyson George James (carting
     contractor)
12 Strangleman Frederick James
13 Tait Douglas
14 Bentley Arthur
15 Green George William
16 Worfolk Walter
17 Fysh Ebenezer

## WHITEFRIARS TERRACE
*From Friars Street to The Friars*
### North side
1 Embling Miss
2 Drew Arthur Henry
3 Newman Miss
4 Lupson Walter J  senior
5 Rowe Mrs
6 Hornigold Charles B
7 Shipp John
9 Regester Jeffrey
10  Greenfield Charles Alfred

11  Haines Edward Walter
12  Emerson John
13  Dawson Sydney
14  Faulkner Miss Annie
13  Bowen William
16  Finch Donald Jack
17  Allen Mrs
18  Bone Martin John
19  Chapman Frederick
20  Sheppardson Samuel

## WHITEHOUSE COTTAGES
*From 29 London Road*
1 Ives Mrs
2 Barrett James
3 Collison Harry
4 Williams Wilfred George
5 Ely Charles William

## WHITENING YARD*
*From North Street*
Shears Arthur Edward Wallace
1 Howlett George
2 Britton Mrs
4 Bunn Benjamin

## WILLIAM STREET
*From 4 Charles Street to 15 Thomas Street*
28 Farrow Mrs
19 Holland Frederick John
1 Oakes John Robert
2 Balls Arthur
3 Groom Joseph
4 Nicholls Edward James Charles
5 Harrison Mrs F
6 Tyzack James Henry
7 Mitchell Albert Edward
8 Ward John
9  Crown James
10  Marshall Mrs
11  Neale Edward Henry

## WILLIAM STREET (continued)

12 Yates Alfred Leonard
13 Catton John William
14 Scruby Mrs Clara
15 Rodwell William
16 Flegg William
17 Greenacre Samuel
18 Nichols Edward

## WINDSOR ROAD

*From 31 London Road to Goodwins Road*
### North side

Castle Albert Edward   (boot repairer)
Pank Alfred. Everard, (fruiterer)
*here is Pleasant Row*
Rout Mrs Annie E  (confectioner)
Macdonald Andrew Peter   (confectioner)
Davison John Ernest   (grocer)
Skerritt James
*here is Keppel Street*
Dickerson Fountain  (electrical engineer
Middleton Mrs Agnes A (shopkeeper)
Walker Charles William (ironmonger)
Lowe Mrs
0 Thurston Walter. James
1a Holman Ernest William (boot repairer)
*here is Victoria Street*
2 Ball Charles M   (baker)
3 —
4 Longman Mrs B
5 —
6 Row Mrs F
7 Wright Frank
*here is Wellington Street*
8 Allflatt Charles Drake   (builder)
9 Green Lewis John
0 Watson James William
1 Murray Sydney John
*here is Douro Street*
2 Leeder Arthur
3 Collins John
4 Arch Benjamin

*here is Windsor Terrace*
### South side
*here is Guanock Terrace*

1 Taylor Harry Leonard
2 Corbett Mrs
3 & 4 Fox John  (general dealer)
5 Link Ernest Edward  (fried fish shop)
6 Parfrement Alfred  (outfitter)
7 Jubey Frederick   (boot maker)
8a Crisp Herbert H  (butcher)
9a Newham Ralph S   (blacksmith)
10a Darby Henry George
11 Watson harry Baden
12a Ellis Frederick
26 Steward James
*here is Garden Row*
**Live & Let Live PH   (George W Ollett)**
4 Crisp Mrs F
3 Fendley Miss M
2 Holland Bertram  (dairyman)
Suckling John  (fruiterer)

### WINDSOR ROW
*From Garden Row*

1 Hewitt George Robert
2 Day Ronald George
3 Greeves William
4 Hawkins Sydney William
5 Fox Henry
6 Coates James
7 Mawby Arthur John
8 Alexander Richard William
9 Price Cyril
10 Lyon Edmund Thomas
11 Garrett Thomas Albert
12 Strutton Mrs
1a Wilson Mrs M
2a Muncaster Sydney

## WINDSOR TERRACE
*From 24 Windsor Road to Hospital Walk*

1 Nicholls Wilfred James
2 Blyth Mrs
3 Fiddy William
4 Meggitt Mrs N
5 Cook Reginald Ernest
6 English George
7 Wilkinson Mrs AV
8 Bocking Hedley Victor
9 Hoare James
10 Smith William Edward
*here is Arthur Street*
11 Webb Thomas
12 Clarke Robert Henry
13 Causton Mrs
14 Panton Charles
15 Burgess Ralph
16 Lown Mrs SF
17 Panton Charles  junior

## WINFARTHING AVENUE
*From Wisbech Road to Diamond Terrace*
### East side

1 Roy Ernest Victor
3 Spooner Tom Taylor
5 Cooke Leonard Clements
7 Adams Stanley Charles
9 Bushell Francis Vernon
11 Hannam Charles
13 Hitch Alfred John
15 Hides Sidney
17 Mortimer Harry
19 Mott Mrs
21 Pooley Arthur Frederick
23 Turner William
25 Hall Geo. Dundonald
27 Rees William Ernest
29 Catchpole John William
31 Ess Charles Henry
### West side
16 Bell Philip Henry

18 Suter Stanley Arthur
20 Dorman James Walter
22 Cook John
24 Greenacre Herbert
26 Goat Stanley
28 Lloyd Geo
30 Hulbert Leslie
32 Wilkinson Mrs
### South side
Grummett George  (Dalton House)
Rout Daniel  (St. John)

## WISBECH ROAD
*From London Road*
### West side

Alexander C & Sons  (cycle dealers)
Auto-Culto Depot
Casserly Miss Beatrice  (confectioner)
Tuddenham's  (fried fish shop)
Smith Louis E  (cabinet maker)
Brown George Robert (Narside)
Brown Henry Herbert (WhiteGables)
**Railway Tavern  (Alfred Ernest Tingle)**
Cresswell Percy A  (Railway Cottage)
Willerson Mrs  (Field Cottage)
1 Walden Walter  (hairdresser)
2 Betts George  (insurance agent)
Richardson Alexander  (Victoria Cottage)
Watson George
Mann Mrs  (May Cottage)
Darrington George  (York Cottage)
Bridges Mrs  (Clarence Cottage)
8 Neave John Thomas
9 Hampton Percy EE  (electrician)
10 Barnes George  (shopkeeper & post office)

### Nelson Terrace
1 Adams Mrs Elizabeth
2 Sutton John
3 Pattern John
4 Adams Stanley

## WISBECH ROAD (continued)

5 Berry Dennis   (boot repairer)

6 Barker Alfred Robert

———

*here is Lancaster Terrace*

17 Morley & Sons  (bakers)

18 Gathercole John Thomas

19 Newstead William  (shopkeeper)

20 Dye Jacob Wing

21 Smith Frederick Lucius

22 Beveridge George  (newsagent)

23 Dickerson Alfred  (fried fish shop)

24 Neal Robert William  (shopkeeper)

Neal Frank   (butcher)  (Fir Cottage)

Barwood George Henry  (signwriter) (Marion Cottage)

27 Morley Ernest George (confectioner)

28 Pooley William

29 Trundle Robert

30 Morley Frank William

31 Morfoot Fred

32 Hill Frederick Charles

33 Clitheroe William

34 Proctor Charles

35 Gibbs Cecil Moston

36 Warnes Miss AE

37 Parnell William

**Jolly Farmers PH  (Phoebe Ess until March 1933, then Harry Winter until July 1933 then Arthur Septimus Bunton)**

25 Twaite Walter. Ernest

26 —

41 Taylor Miss

Dixie Frank Reginald  (Portland House)

*here is Portland Place*

45 Thurston Jonathan

46 Avis Frederick William  (fried fish shop)

47 Ketteringham Arthur John (shopkeeper)

48 Snelling George

Plowright Mrs (The Oaks)

*here is Queen's Avenue*

Hill Richard R   (Holme Villa)

Kirman William  (sluice keeper) (Nar Valley House)

Adams Joseph Albert (South House)

Sheriff James (White House)

Algar C & Sons   (motor engineers)

**Portland Arms PH   (Charles H Algar)**

### East side

King's Lynn Gas Co. (works)

West Norfolk Farmers' Manure & Chemical Co-operative Co. Ltd

Wright Bertie Robert (Gate house)

*here is Saddlebow Road*

Union Baptist Church

Thornley William  (taxi-cab proprietor) (Belmont)

Bragg Leonard G (Jeslen)

Morley's Garage   (motor engineers)

Copeman Herbert (Edaw)

Gray Ralph M (Magnusville)

Bayston Leslie (Burley)

61 Gates Ted

63 Ashby Walter

*here is Metcalf Avenue*

65 Smith Bernard Frederick

67 Major Joseph

69 Few Charles Harry

71 Hancock John

73 Ely Arthur

75 Simpole Reginald John

77 Stinton Samuel

79 Snelling George

*here is Bunnett Avenue*

81 Cooper George

83 Faulkner Joseph

85 Ebbs James Henry

87 Henry Charles Frank

Cooper Roller Bearings Co. Ltd

Bedford Gustavus   (dairyman) (Bridge Farm)

## WOOD STREET

*From 10 St. James' Place to 53 South Street*

### South side

1 Garrett Robert Charles
2 Juby Frederick William
3 Ebbs Frederick Charles
4 McKessock William James
5 Farr James Richard
6 Anderson Frederick
7 Anderson James
8 Smith George Hubert
9 Rolph Arthur
10 Wilkinson Mrs
11 Bouch Samuel A   (baker)
12 Coleman Ernest Robert
13 Neal William
14 Pickett Harry E
15 Drayton Mrs S
16 Bouch William
17 Rowe James Frederick
18 Moore Alfred
19 Evetts Mrs S
20 Wittred Reginald Victor
21 Ollett Henry William
22 Burrows Arthur William

### North side

20 Tyzack Charles Robert
21 Harris Arthur
22a Casey Frederick Harry
*here are Wanford Cottages*
23 Kirk Mrs H
24 Stanford Herbert William
25 Skerritt William
26 Largen William
27 Chapman James
28 Jarvis George
29 Juby Arthur
30 Atkins John William
31 Fysh James
32 Docking Mrs
33 Juby Charles
33a Brundle George Frederick
King's Lynn Corporation (depot)

The Gaywood river passes under the Wootton Road beside Riverside. In 1936 a new bridge (generally referred to as the 'Stone Bridge') was built in order to take the increase of traffic into and out of the town.

This new RH Guest garage at 123 Wootton Road opened in 1934 to replace the original from 1928 when the business was first inaugurated. It later was re-named Peter Guest.

**WOODWARK AVENUE**

*From Loke Road*

North side

1 Griggs Herbert
2 Riches Sidney
3 Fretwell Wilfred William
4 Dunger Horace William,
5 Howlett John
6 Minister Ernest
7 Bailey James
8 Mendham Victor John
9 Massen John William
10 Fisher Mrs

*here is Edma Street*

11 Gathercole Alfred Milner
12 Grant George
13 Reynolds Thomas Victor
14 Chase Matthew
15 Gaskin Sydney

16 Moulton Ernest Robert

South side

17 Honeywood Daniel
18 Hayles William
19 Massingham Frederick William
20 Pegg John
21 Reynolds William
22 Butcher Robert

*here is Edma Street*

23 Ransom Samuel
24 Garford Joseph
25 Smith Charles A
26 Bridges George Thomas
27 Drew Frederick
28 Thrower Stephen
29 Smith Sidney
30 Webber Benjamin
31 Sillis Ernest
32 Johnson George William

Bensley's Auto & Radio at 30, Wootton Road in the 1930s.

## WOOTTON LANE♦

*From Wootton Road*

Brown Derrick William (Kinnoull)

Maries Walter (Artlegarth)

### Grange Houses

1 Eagle Willis
2 Raby Edward
3 Wiseman Eric Stanley
4 Mallett Hector
5 Tasker Ales. George
6 Poll Gilbert Arthur

McLean Joseph T (1 Grange Cottages)
Brown Ernest R (2 Grange Cottages)

## WOOTTON ROAD♦

*From 83 Lynn Road*

West side

1 **Cock Inn** **(Mrs Frances Farmer)**
3 Marsters Arthur L  (grocer)
5 Smith Charles L  (butcher)
**White Horse  PH   (William J Williamson)**

*here is River Lane*

11 Ewen John
13 Copeman Mrs
35 Rivett Mrs H
17 Turvey George James
19 Bocking John Preston   (builder)
21 Carter Herbert
23 Watts Herbert William
25 Fillenham Albert Edmnd.  (shopkeeper and post office)
29 Chilvers John James
31 Robinson Mrs K M
33 Hardwick William Jonathan

In 1937 driver and ticket collector take a break as the South Wootton bus waits to return to Lynn at Wootton Gap (the junction of the Grimston Road and the Hunstanton Road - then the main road via Castle Rising).

### WOOTTON ROAD♦ (continued)

35 Leman Alfred. Thomas
37 Greenacre Marriott George
39 Archer George Alfred
41 Beart Alfred Charles
43 Overton John
45 Burn Arden
47 Walker George Henry
49 Hayes William Thomas
51 Folkes Arthur G
53 Davey William Edward
55 Holman  Mrs Kathleen  (ladies' hairdresser)
57 Seaman Charles  (boot repairer)
59 Smith Charles L
61 Staley Abraham Joseph
63 Crome Hector
65 Rivett William Robert
67 Smeed Frederick Matthew
69 Bissell William John
71 Bonney Charles Ronald
73 Hugman Jack Woodward
75 Linford Stanley
77 Brown Sidney Frank
79 Fear Wilfred Charles

81 Ablett Samuel Charles
83 Betts Stanley Cyril
85 Brown William Harry
87 & 89 Durrant Winston G   (butcher)
*here is Methuen Avenue*
91 Brear Stephen Martin   (fruiterer)
93 —
95 Carter William Leonard
97 Fogarty Edmnd. MB, BCh, BAO, LMDub (physician & surgery)
99 Tyers William
101 Parker Gerald Ernest
103 White Albert B
105 Butcher Herbert George
107 —
109 Brailli Rudolph
111 Cox Percy Frederick
113 Lane Albert Edward B
115 Balls Cyril Charles
117 Alvis Misses
119 Foreman Sidney
121 Day Arthur Edward
123 Guest RH   (motor engineer)
125 Middleton John  (baker)
*here is Beulah Street*

## WOOTTON ROAD♦ (continued)

127 Skinner Frederick Lewis
129 Driver Edward
131 Williams Oliver
133 Mason Albert Edward
135 Underhill Mrs
137 Regester Charles T
139 Howard Joseph James
141 Foster James
143 Ollett Thomas James
145 Fendley Miss
147 Bray Percival B
149 Youngs John Charles
151 Gibson Mrs E
153 Sheppard Arthur CK
155 Donaldson Alec
157 Edmunds Thomas Walter
159 Rippengill Mrs
161 Curson Bullen (insurance agent)
163 Adams Matthew
165 Medlock Walter
167 Frost Alfred
169 Hirst William Stanley
171 Gunston Albert John
173 Sheldrake Henry
175 Hill Percy Albert
177 Ward George
179 Tovell Samuel Charles
181 Rudd Horace
183 Rush Edward
185 Adams Miss
187 Laurence Miss
189 Humphrey Mrs
191 Bridges Miss
193 Scase William Henry
195 Harrison John
197 Allen William Arthur
201 Palmer Andrew
*here is Riverside*
203 Hill Charles J
205 Bishop Robert Cecil
207 Fawcett Guy Stafford

209 Croot Mrs
*here is Marsh Lane*
211 Wharton Ernest
213 Bather Charles Herbert
215 Armes George
217 Culey John EV
219 Culey Benjamin G
221 Green George Reginald
223 Cornell Victor B
225 Bartlett Alexander James
227 Cann Walter
229 Valentine Reginald. Arthur
231 Belton Robert John
233 Kirby Cecil
235 Anderson Walter
237 Kirby George
239 Gethin John Henry
Starling Ernest Frederick (Marajon)
Breeze Ernest (Catriona)
Turner Charles Harold (Hillcroft)
Vanderloo Hendrik (Norlyn)
245 Young Herbert
247 Tilford Mrs
249 Cox William
251 Cawston Alfred
253 Hill Arthur E
255 Trollope Thomas
*here is Mill Lane*
257 Tovell Mrs
263 Barnshaw Frank
265 Fendley Harry
267 Hewitt Charles Young
269 Smith Harry Robert
271 Storey Robert L
273 Gunthorpe George Russell
275 Reeve E C
277 Norgate Cecil Edward
281 Pointer L (confectioner)
283 Wilkinson Rd. Hepworth
285 Valentine Tom Arthur
Empire Motor Road Service Station
(George W Hildon, proprietor)

## WOOTTON ROAD♦ (continued)

303 Hildon George William
*here is Empire Avenue*
305 Snelling Robert Dix
Catleugh John Harwood MBE (The Grange)
*here is Wootton Lane*
311 Andrew William Henry
313 Marsters Walter
315 Fyfe Mrs
317 Burn Fenwick Walter
319 Bradfield Edward William
321 Adams Walter
323 Jermyn Bertram W
325 Rawlin John
327 Osborn Matthew Herbert
329 White Henry Alfred
331 Anderson James
Askew Albert V (Green Lawn)
333 Regester Miss
335 Allflat Keeble
337 Taylor Edward Watson
339 Thornley James C
341 Murrell Mrs Sophia (refreshment rooms)
47 Blake Bros. (motor cycle agents)
49 **New Inn (William Ford)**

### East side
Watling Frederick J (hairdresser)
& 6 Fysh Charles (fried fish shop)
Rudd Henry
0 Neal Sidney
2 Hudson Herbert
4 Grantham Edwin (grocer)
**Frosts Buildings**
Grantham Edwin
Leader William Cecil
Williamson William Frederick

———

8 Rudd Sydney
0 Cushing Charles W
2 Bowles Howard Albert
4 English Herbert
6 Norton Mrs E

28 Neal John
30 Bensley H (motor car repairs)
Bowden Thomas William (Avondale)
Moore Reginald. (Tyn-y-Groes)
Ridehalgh Mrs (Bettws-y-Coed)
Bann William (The Rest)
Mallett William Harold (Yvonne)
Copeman Frederick
32 Lusher Robert
*here is Lavender Terrace*
Barrett CG & Co. (laundry)
34 Blackwell Herbert
36 Lister Alfred. John
38 Green Reginald
40 Colman Arthur Edward
42 Pigott Robert
44 Barrett Charles G
46 Green Arnold
48 Lake Mrs G
50 Rose Charles
52 Fysh Arthur
54 Shipp Walter
56 Taylor Bert
58 Uloth Alexander Wilmot MC, MA, MBBCh,
MRCS, LRCP (physician & surgeon & medical
officer & public vaccinator
NCC Guardians Committee)
60 Child Frederick Joseph
*here is Rosebery Avenue*
62 Hayes Cyril
64 Blomfield Sidney
66 Porter Walter. Alfred
68 Sursham Henry David
70 Cook Mrs H
72 Cohen Hermann
74 Spinks Henry William
76 Reeve Leonard Charles
78 Thompson Harry
80 Morris Mrs ML
82 Hanwell Sydney
84 Harding William Samuel
(inspector, RSPCA)

## WOOTTON ROAD◆ (continued)

86 Goddard Alfred
88 Johnson Reginald
90 Whitmore Miss D
92 Seaman Mrs
94 Burnell Mrs
96 Hoare James Barnes
98 Whisker Charles James
100 Alcock John E
102 Topple Harold Ernest
104 Manning Frank
106 Bray William John
108 Aylmer Miss
108 Hilditch Miss
110 Gamble Karl Edward
112 Sunderland Mrs
114 Knape John
116 Sexton Archibald
118 Barnaby Herbert
120 Heney John
122 Gore William
124 Rudd Herbert W
126 Goodbody Henry
128 Green Paine Franklin
130 Metcalf Arnold
132 Hampton Mrs S
134 Hampton Raymond FR
136 Durrant John E
138 Crisp Charles
Mindham Herbert John  (Highfields)
160 Regester Sidney Charles
162 Fillenham Lewis Arthur
164 Bentley Ernest
166 Widger Mrs
Proctor William Leslie (Knockawn)
Buttle Thomas George (Haven Bungalow)
Osborne Henry (The Rest)
Barnard John Edward
Potter John (MarJohn)
Hawes Ernest (Jubilee)
192 Savage William Robert
194 Osborne Thomas Henry

196 Pryor Harry E
198 Redhead James
200 Auker James
202 Holden Thomas
204 Snoad Mrs
206 Mann John William
208 Lake Reginald
210 Bishop Harry
212 Golden William Frederick
214 Wilson John Thomas
216 Read Rowland S
218 Brooker John
Burrow Thomas William  (Mill Cottage)
224 Greenhalgh Arthur
226 Mears Mrs
228 Rayer Harold Thomas (insurance agent)
232 Sedler HW
234 Black William Desmond
236 Fell Robert Cecil
238 Searjeant Joseph
240 Thompson Arthur Roland
242 Pycroft Henry
244 Butler Cyril E
246 Lacey Jack
248 Trevitt James
250 Carr Ernest James
252 Dawson Horace W
254 Middleton Ellis
256 Torbell Russell Henry
258 Adlam Walter
260 Sexton Henry William
262 Popkiss C
264 Pritchard G  Edmund
266 Marsh Harold
268 Goldsmith Eric Walter
270 Herrington Reginald
272 Atkins Oliver
274 Cooper Frederick Eyre
276 White Frederick Charles
278 Wallis Charles Edward
280 Wilson Bertie
282 Swann. Eric Lister

## WOOTTON ROAD♦ (continued)

84 Bremner Bernard Eustace
86 Smith Gilbert Steer
88 Clark Robert Douglas
90 Gregory David
92 Cobbold Henry George
94 Donaldson George
96 Gilchrist Charles
98 Martin Donald Benjamin  BSc
00 Squires Cecil Smith
Burgoyne William Alexander  (Overstone)
12 Harrison Frederick G
18 Chilvers Reginald Curtis
20 Tassell Reginald William
22 —

## WYATT STREET
*From 8 Paxton Terrace to*
*17 Coburg Street*
### East side

Old Town Wall  PH  (William Stoakley)
Creek Mrs
Grenowath & Son  (furniture repository)
0 Hewitt John Thomas
1 Burton John
1 Burton Brothers  (window cleaners)
### West side
Johnson Mrs
Dickerson Mrs
Hewett John Robert
Hewson Miss
Eglinton Obed
Belcher Charles
Twaite Robert Philip
6 Pemment Mrs
5 Smith Frederick
4 Barrett William Frederick
3 Frost Mrs
2  Fisher Benjamin

## YORK ROAD
*From Chase Avenue to*
*71 Vancouver Avenue*
### North side

Akers Thomas Alfred. (Marbaix)
Harrison William (insurance agent)  (Domum)
Linford William Henry  (Suncote)
7a Anderson Arthur Albert
Robertson Reginald. (Holme Dene)
9  Dye James
10  Townsend James Edward
11  Thorne Bert
12  Cork William Thomas
13  Green William George
14  Mortimer Arthur
15  Lane Frederick William
### South side
1  McCulloch Mrs Emily
2  Emerson Redvers W
3  Bullen Arthur
4  Shafto Thomas
5  Nichols John George
6  Hilling William Charles
7  Sheppardson Mrs H

### ENVIRONS OF KING'S LYNN
Hodgson Raymond Percy  (farmer)  (White House Farm)

163

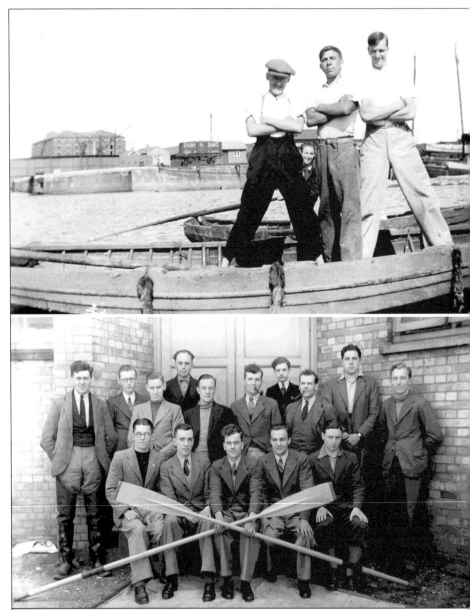

TOP: Very many Northenders were fishing (or related to) families. Most were very poor by modern definitions of deprivation. Most could not afford to take (unpaid) holidays. Sundays were the only day when they would have a 'holiday' and swimming in the dock was about as exotic as it got! Pictured messing about in rowing boats are (left to right): Wal Blade, Bill Booth, Tom Hillard and Bill Norton at the back.

BOTTOM: For those of a higher social standing there was the Neptune Rowing Club.